An Illustrated Review of the

RESPIRATORY SYSTEM

Glenn F. Bastian

HarperCollinsCollegePublishers

Executive Editor: Bonnie Roesch
Cover Designer: Kay Petronio
Production Manager: Bob Cooper
Printer and Binder: Malloy Lithographing, Inc.
Cover Printer: The Lehigh Press, Inc.

AN ILLUSTRATED REVIEW OF THE RESPIRATORY SYSTEM

by Glenn F. Bastian

Copyright © 1994 HarperCollins College Publishers

Library of Congress Cataloging-in-Publication Data
Bastian, Glenn F.
          An illustrated review of the respiratory system / Glenn
     F. Bastian.
               p.   cm.
          Includes bibliographical references.
          ISBN: 0-06-501709-9
               1. Respiratory organs—Physiology—Outlines, syllabi, etc.
     2. Respiratory organs—Physiology—Atlases. I. Title.
          [DNLM: 1. Respiratory system—examination questions.
     2. Respiratory System —atlases. WF 18 B326i 1994]
     QP121.B32 1994
     612.2'076—dc20   —dc20
     DNLM/DLC
     for Library of Congress   93–4204
                                                                      CIP

94 95 96 9 8 7 6 5 4 3 2 1

In Memory of
James B. Webster

CONTENTS

LIST OF TOPICS & ILLUSTRATIONS

Text: One page of text is devoted to each of the following topics. *Illustrations are listed in italics.*

PREFACE

An Illustrated Review of Anatomy and Physiology is a series of ten books written to help students effectively review the structure and function of the human body. Each book in the series is devoted to a different body system.

My objective in writing these books is to make very complex subjects accessible and nonthreatening by presenting material in manageable-size bits (one topic per page) with clear, simple illustrations to assist the many students who are primarily visual learners. Designed to supplement established texts, they may be used as a student aid to jog the memory, to quickly recall the essentials of each major topic, and to practice naming structures in preparation for exams.

INNOVATIVE FEATURES OF THE BOOK

(1) Each major topic is confined to one page of text.

A unique feature of this book is that each topic is confined to one page and the material is presented in outline form with the key terms in boldface or italic typeface. This makes it easy to scan quickly the major points of any given topic. The student can easily get an overview of the topic and then zero in on a particular point that needs clarification.

(2) Each page of text has an illustration on the facing page.

Because each page of text has its illustration on the facing page, there is no need to flip through the book looking for the illustration that is referred to in the text ("see Figure X on page xx"). The purpose of the illustration is to clarify a central idea discussed in the text. The images are simple and clear, the lines are bold, and the labels are in a large type. Each illustration deals with a well-defined concept, allowing for a more focused study.

PHYSIOLOGY TOPICS (1 text page : 1 illustration)
Each main topic in physiology is limited to one page of text with one supporting illustration on the facing page.

ANATOMY TOPICS (1 text page : several illustrations)
For complex anatomical structures a good illustration is more valuable than words. So, for topics dealing with anatomy, there are often several illustrations for one text topic.

(3) Unlabeled illustrations have been included.
In Part II, all illustrations have been repeated without their labels. This allows a student to test his or her visual knowledge of the basic concepts.

(4) A Pronunciation Guide has been included.
Phonetic spellings of unfamiliar terms are listed in a separate section, unlike other textbooks where they are usually found in the glossary or spread throughout the text. The student may use this guide for pronunciation drill or as a quick review of basic vocabulary.

(5) A glossary has been included.
Most textbooks have glossaries that include terms for all of the systems of the body. It is convenient to have all of the key terms for one system in a single glossary.

ACKNOWLEDGMENTS

I would like to thank the reviewers of the manuscript for this book who carefully critiqued the text and illustrations for their effectiveness: William Kleinelp, Middlesex County College; Robert Smith, University of Missouri, St. Louis, and St. Louis Community College, Forest Park; and Pamela Monaco, Molloy College. Their help and advice are greatly appreciated. Kay Petronio is to be commended for her handsome cover design and Bob Cooper has my gratitude for keeping the production moving smoothly. Finally, I am greatly indebted to my editor Bonnie Roesch for her willingness to try a new idea, and for her support throughout this project. I invite students and instructors to send any comments and suggestions for enhancements or changes to this book to me, in care of HarperCollins, so that future editions can continue to meet your needs.

Glenn Bastian

An Illustrated Review of the RESPIRATORY SYSTEM

1 Structures

STRUCTURES / Overview

Respiration Respiration has two different meanings: (1) the exchange of oxygen and carbon dioxide between the atmosphere and the cells of an organism; (2) the utilization of oxygen in the mitochondria of cells for the production of energy (ATP). The second type is called *cellular respiration*.

RESPIRATORY STRUCTURES
Upper Respiratory System The nose, pharynx (throat), and associated structures.

Lower Respiratory System The larynx, trachea, bronchi, and lungs.
Conducting Portion Structures that warm, moisten, and filter the incoming air.
Respiratory Portion Structures that contain air sacs (alveoli) where gas exchange occurs.

Lungs The two lungs consist mostly of microscopic air sacs (about 150 million per lung).

The Respiratory Pump The structures involved in moving air in and out of the lungs include the rib cage, the pleural membranes, the respiratory muscles (diaphragm, etc.), and the elastic tissues of the lungs.

RESPIRATORY PROCESSES
Pulmonary Ventilation Breathing.
Inspiration (Inhalation) The flow of air into the lungs.
Expiration (Exhalation) The flow of air out of the lungs.

Gas Exchange
External Respiration Exchange of gases between the lungs and the blood.
Internal Respiration Exchange of gases between the blood and the cells.

Gas Transport Gas transport is a function of the cardiovascular system.
Oxygen Most oxygen (98.5%) is combined with hemoglobin in red blood cells.
Carbon Dioxide Most carbon dioxide (70%) is dissolved in plasma as bicarbonate ions.

Cellular Respiration The utilization of oxygen by cells for the production of ATP.
Glycolysis The breakdown of 1 glucose molecule to form 2 molecules of pyruvic acid.
Formation of Acetyl Coenzyme A The conversion of pyruvic acid into acetyl coenzyme A.
Krebs Cycle (Citric Acid Cycle) The stepwise breakdown of citric acid into oxaloacetic acid.
Electron Transport Chain The passing of electrons along a chain of carrier molecules to an oxygen molecule; there is a stepwise release of energy for the production of ATP. Oxygen must be present to accept the electrons at the end of the chain and combine with hydrogen ions to form water. This mechanism for producing ATP is called *oxidative phosphorylation*. Most of the ATP produced by cells is produced by oxidative phosphorylation (32 of the 36 ATPs produced by the oxidation of 1 glucose molecule), so it is extremely important that the respiratory system supply body cells with sufficient oxygen.

FUNCTIONS OF THE RESPIRATORY SYSTEM
Provides Oxygen Oxygen is necessary for oxidative phosphorylation (ATP production).
Eliminates Carbon Dioxide High blood carbon dioxide levels cause acidity (low pH).
Conditions Air The airways warm, moisten, and clean the incoming air.
Produces Sounds The vocal cords in the larynx and other structures produce speech.
Senses Odors Olfactory receptors are located on the roof of the nasal cavities.

RESPIRATORY STRUCTURES

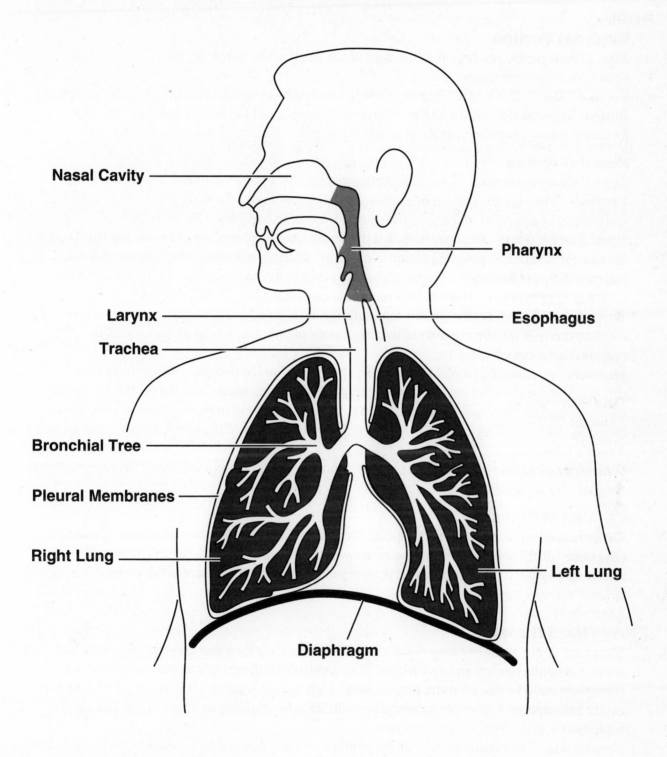

Nasal Cavity

Pharynx

Larynx

Esophagus

Trachea

Bronchial Tree

Pleural Membranes

Right Lung

Left Lung

Diaphragm

STRUCTURES / Nose and Pharynx (Throat)

NOSE

External Portion

Root   The superior attachment of the nose at the forehead between the eyes.

Apex   The tip of the nose.

Dorsum Nasi   The rounded anterior border of the the nose, connecting the root and the apex.

Bridge   The superior portion of the dorsum nasi; superior to the nasal bones.

External Nares (singular: *Naris*) also called *Nostrils*   External opening into the nose.

Nasal Cavities

The nasal cavities consist of two chambers separated by a partition (nasal septum).

Vestibule   The anterior portion of each nasal cavity just inside the nostril. It is lined with skin and contains hairs called *vibrissae*, which remove coarse particles from incoming air.

Nasal Septum   The vertical partition that divides the nasal cavity into right and left sides (called the nasal fossae). The anterior portion is made of cartilage; the remainder is made of bone.

Internal Nares (Choanae) Two openings that connect the nasal cavities to the nasopharynx.

Conchae (Turbinates)   Three scroll-like elevations on the lateral wall of each nasal cavity. They are called the superior, middle, and inferior nasal conchae, according to their location. The conchae increase the surface area of the respiratory membrane, which helps to condition the incoming air more efficiently.

Meatuses   A series of groovelike passageways formed by the conchae. Ducts from the paranasal sinuses and the nasolacrimal (tear) ducts drain secretions into the meatuses. As air whirls around the conchae and meatuses, it is warmed by blood in the capillaries. Mucus secreted by goblet cells moistens the air and traps dust particles. Cilia move mucus to the pharynx, where it is swallowed.

Olfactory Epithelium   Olfactory (smell) receptors lie in the membrane lining the superior nasal conchae and adjacent septum.

Paranasal Sinuses

The paranasal sinuses are air-filled spaces located in the maxillary, frontal, ethmoid, and sphenoid bones of the skull. Small openings allow mucus to drain into the nasal cavities. Sinuses reduce the weight of the skull and serve as resonant chambers for voice production.

PHARYNX (Throat)

The pharynx is a funnel-shaped passageway about 5 inches long that connects the nasal and oral cavities with the trachea and esophagus. It is divided into three regions based on location.

Nasopharynx   The nasopharynx is continuous with the nasal cavity; it is posterior to the nasal cavity and superior to the soft palate. The auditory tube (Eustachian tube) opens into the nasopharynx.

Oropharynx   The middle portion of the pharynx; it lies posterior to the oral cavity (mouth) and extends from the soft palate inferiorly to the level of the hyoid bone. The opening from the mouth into the oropharynx is called the *fauces*. Two pairs of tonsils, the palatine and lingual tonsils, are found in the oropharynx.

Laryngopharynx   The lowest portion of the pharynx. It extends downward from the hyoid bone and becomes continuous with the esophagus (food tube) and larynx (voice box).

4

NOSE AND PHARYNX

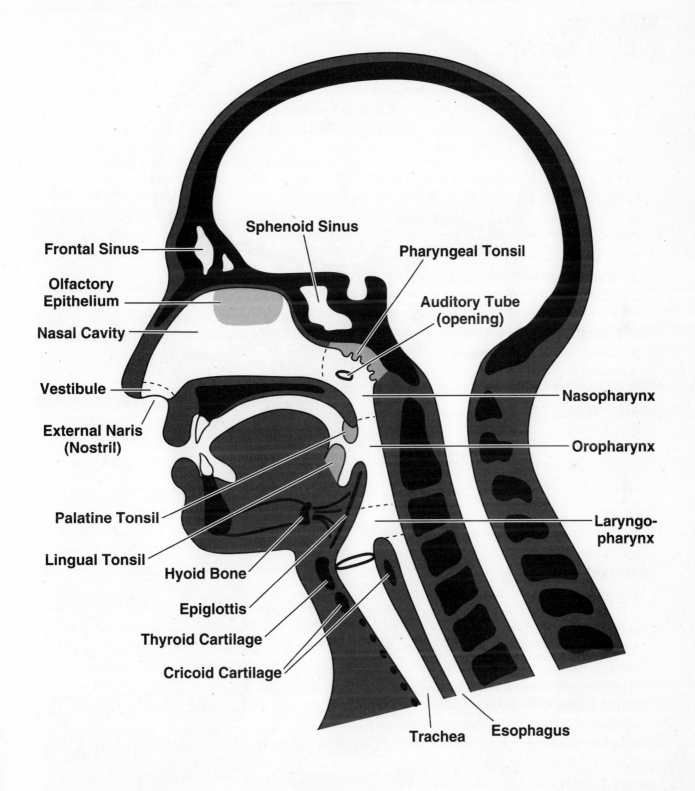

Frontal Sinus

Sphenoid Sinus

Pharyngeal Tonsil

Olfactory Epithelium

Auditory Tube (opening)

Nasal Cavity

Vestibule

Nasopharynx

External Naris (Nostril)

Oropharynx

Palatine Tonsil

Laryngo-pharynx

Lingual Tonsil

Hyoid Bone

Epiglottis

Thyroid Cartilage

Cricoid Cartilage

Trachea

Esophagus

NASAL CAVITIES AND SINUSES

Cranium
Frontal Section

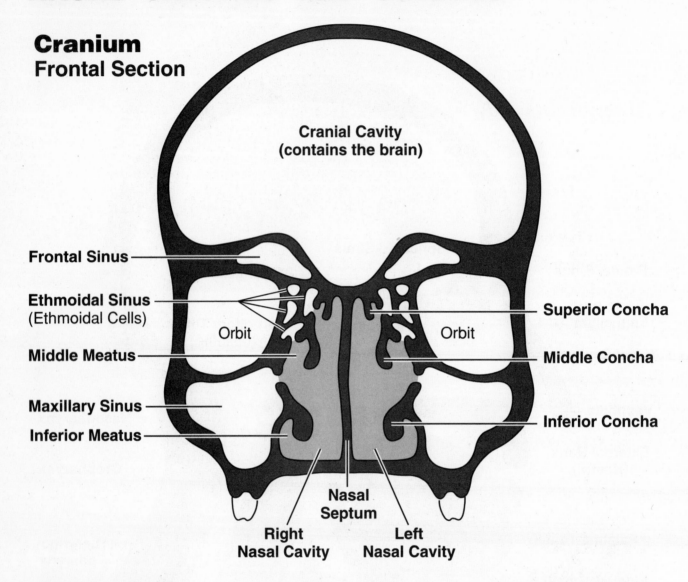

Cranial Cavity
(contains the brain)

Frontal Sinus

Ethmoidal Sinus
(Ethmoidal Cells)

Orbit

Middle Meatus

Maxillary Sinus

Inferior Meatus

Superior Concha

Orbit

Middle Concha

Inferior Concha

Nasal
Septum

Right
Nasal Cavity

Left
Nasal Cavity

Nasal Cavity
Lateral View

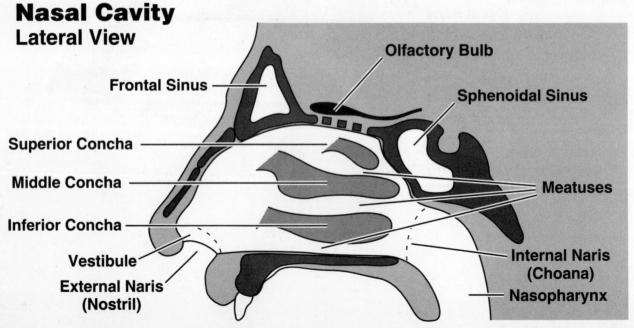

Olfactory Bulb

Frontal Sinus

Sphenoidal Sinus

Superior Concha

Middle Concha

Meatuses

Inferior Concha

Vestibule

External Naris
(Nostril)

Internal Naris
(Choana)

Nasopharynx

PARANASAL SINUSES

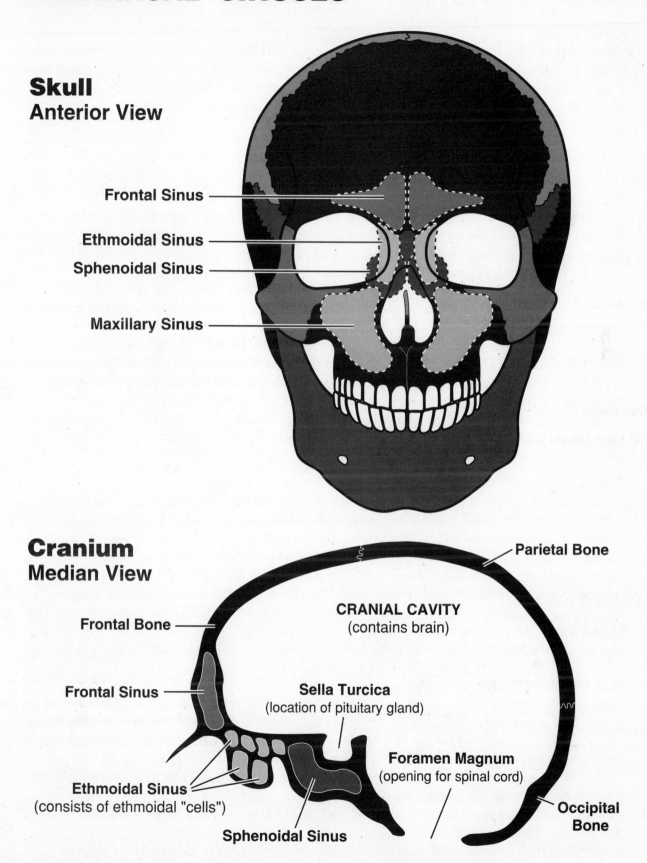

Skull
Anterior View

Frontal Sinus

Ethmoidal Sinus

Sphenoidal Sinus

Maxillary Sinus

Cranium
Median View

Parietal Bone

CRANIAL CAVITY
(contains brain)

Frontal Bone

Sella Turcica
(location of pituitary gland)

Frontal Sinus

Foramen Magnum
(opening for spinal cord)

Ethmoidal Sinus
(consists of ethmoidal "cells")

Occipital Bone

Sphenoidal Sinus

note : maxillary sinus is not visible in this illustration

STRUCTURES

The larynx, or voice box, is a short passageway that connects the pharynx (throat) with the trachea (windpipe). It houses the vocal cords, which are used for sound production. The larynx, which lies in the midline of the neck anterior to the 4th through the 6th cervical vertebrae, has a wall composed of nine pieces of cartilage.

Glottis   The glottis is the portion of the larynx most involved with sound production. It consists of a pair of folds of mucous membrane, the *vocal folds* (true vocal cords), and the *rima glottidis* (the opening between the vocal folds).

Cartilages (9 Pieces)

Epiglottis (Epiglottic Cartilage)   A large, leaf-shaped piece of elastic cartilage. The stem portion is attached to the anterior rim of the thyroid cartilage; the leaf portion is unattached and free to move up and down like a trap door. During swallowing, the epiglottis forms a lid over the glottis; this covers the opening to the larynx, preventing the entrance of food.

Thyroid Cartilage   Two fused plates of hyaline cartilage that form the anterior wall of the larynx. The thyroid cartilage causes the *laryngeal prominence*, a protrusion of the anterior part of the neck.

Cricoid Cartilage   Cricoid comes from the Greek work meaning "ring." It is the most inferior of the cartilages of the larynx and is shaped like a signet ring with the band part facing anteriorly.

Arytenoid Cartilages (2)   The paired arytenoid cartilages influence the positions and tensions of the vocal folds (true vocal cords). They attach to the vocal folds and the intrinsic pharyngeal muscles.

Corniculate Cartilages (2)   The paired corniculate cartilages are horn-shaped pieces of elastic cartilage. They are located at the apex of each arytenoid cartilage.

Cuneiform Cartilages (2)   The paired cuneiform cartilages are wedge-shaped elastic cartilages anterior to the corniculate cartilages.

Folds

Vocal Folds (True Vocal Cords)   The vocal folds are a pair of mucous membrane folds located below the ventricular folds; they are concerned with voice production. Each fold (vocal cord) consists of a connective tissue band covered by mucous membrane and extends from the thyroid cartilage to an arytenoid cartilage. The space between the vocal folds is called the *rima glottidis*.

Ventricular Folds (False Vocal Cords)   The ventricular folds are superior to the vocal folds; they consist of two thick folds of mucous membrane. They are part of the mechanism that closes the larynx during swallowing; they also function in holding the breath against abdominal pressure. The space between the ventricular folds is called the *rima vestibuli*. The lateral expansion of the middle portion of the laryngeal cavity between the vocal and ventricular folds is called the *laryngeal sinus*.

VOICE PRODUCTION

Sound   Elastic ligaments within the mucous membranes of the vocal folds are stretched between the thyroid and arytenoid cartilages like the strings on a guitar. If air is directed against the vocal folds, they vibrate and set up sound waves in the column of air in the pharynx, nose, and mouth.

Loudness   The greater the pressure of air, the louder the sound.

Pitch   Pitch is controlled by the tension on the vocal folds. When pulled taut by muscles, the vocal folds vibrate more rapidly, resulting in a higher pitch.

Resonance   The pharynx, mouth, nasal cavity, and paranasal sinuses all act as resonating chambers that give the voice its human and individual qualities.

Vowel Sounds and Enunciation   Constricting and relaxing muscles in the wall of the pharynx produces vowel sounds; muscles of the face, tongue, and lips are involved in enunciation.

LARYNX
Vocal Folds (Vocal Cords)

Midsagittal Section

Superior View

anterior — Epiglottis

Vocal Folds
(Vocal Cords)

Ventricular Folds
(False Vocal Cords)

Rima Glottidis

Cuneiform Cartilage

Corniculate Cartilage

posterior

Frontal Section

Ventricular Folds
(False Vocal Cords)

Arytenoid
Cartilage

Thyroid
Cartilage

Vocal Folds
(Vocal Cords)

Cricoid
Cartilage

Trachea   Esophagus

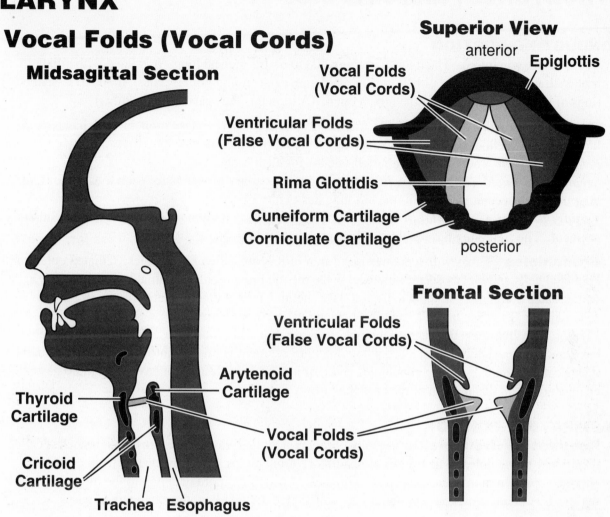

Cartilages of the Larynx

Lateral View

Hyoid Bone

Thyroid
Cartilage

Cricoid
Cartilage

C-shaped
Cartilage Rings
(Trachea)

Anterior View

Epiglottis

Hyoid Bone

Thyroid Cartilage

Posterior View

Corniculate
Cartilage

Arytenoid
Cartilage

Cricoid Cartilage

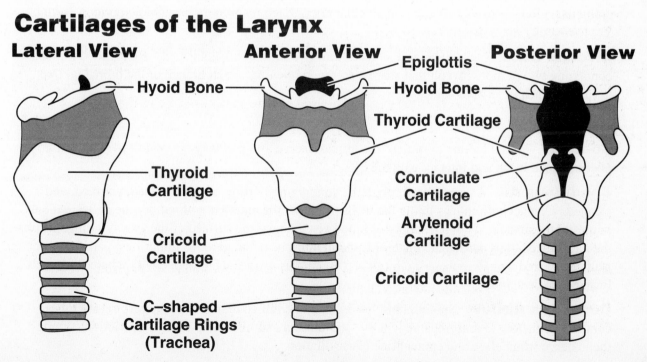

STRUCTURES / Bronchial Tree

CONDUCTING PORTION

Trachea (windpipe) The trachea is about 10 cm (4 1/2 inches) long. It is lined with ciliated pseudostratified columnar epithelium and many mucus-secreting goblet cells. About 20 C-shaped rings of hyaline cartilage keep the lumen open. (A lumen is the space within a tube.)

Bronchi (singular: Bronchus) The trachea divides into two primary bronchi, which enter the lungs. The bronchi divide repeatedly, giving rise to a bronchial tree.
Primary Bronchi There is one primary bronchus for each lung.
Secondary Bronchi (Lobar Bronchi) There is one secondary bronchus for each lobe. The right lung has three secondary bronchi; the left lung has two.
Tertiary Bronchi (Segmental Bronchi) There is one tertiary bronchus for each bronchopulmonary segment. The right lung has ten tertiary bronchi; the left lung has eight.

Bronchioles Tubes with a diameter of 5 mm or less are called bronchioles. Ciliated columnar epithelial cells and mucus-secreting goblet cells line the bronchioles; terminal bronchioles are lined with ciliated columnar epithelial cells, but lack the mucus-secreting goblet cells.
Bronchioles Branches of the tertiary bronchi are called bronchioles.
Terminal Bronchioles Bronchioles branch, forming terminal bronchioles. There is one terminal bronchiole for each lobule (each bronchopulmonary segment is divided into many small compartments called lobules). Since bronchioles and terminal bronchioles do not have alveoli, no gas exchange occurs in this portion of the bronchial tree.

RESPIRATORY PORTION

Respiratory Bronchioles Terminal bronchioles subdivide into microscopic branches called respiratory bronchioles. The linings of respiratory bronchioles gradually change from ciliated cuboidal epithelium to squamous epithelium as they penetrate more deeply into the lungs. Saccular regions lined with squamous epithelium are called alveoli and allow the exchange of gases.

Alveolar Ducts The number of alveoli in a respiratory bronchiole gradually increases as the bronchiole penetrates deeper into the lungs. When the alveoli are no longer separated by cuboidal epithelial cells, the airway is called an alveolar duct. Each respiratory bronchiole divides, forming 2 – 11 alveolar ducts (atria).

Alveolar Sacs Each alveolar duct leads into two or more alveolar sacs — expanded regions containing two or more alveoli that share a common opening. Each branch of the bronchial tree ultimately ends as an alveolar sac.

FUNCTIONS

Conduit The conducting portion of the airways serve as a pathway or conduit by which atmospheric air can reach and interact with the blood.

Conditions Air As air flows through the conducting portion, it is moistened, warmed, and cleaned. Contact with mucus lining the walls moistens the air, so it will not dry the delicate membranes of the alveoli. The rich supply of blood vessels near the surface of the airway linings warms the air. Mucus traps particulate matter (dust and microbes) and gaseous impurities; particulate matter is phagocytized by macrophages; cilia sweep the mucus toward the mouth cavity where it is swallowed or expectorated.

Regulates Airflow Smooth muscles regulate the lumen diameter of the respiratory tubes, controlling airflow. Parasympathetic nerve stimulation and histamine cause constriction; sympathetic nerve stimulation and epinephrine cause dilation.

BRONCHIAL TREE

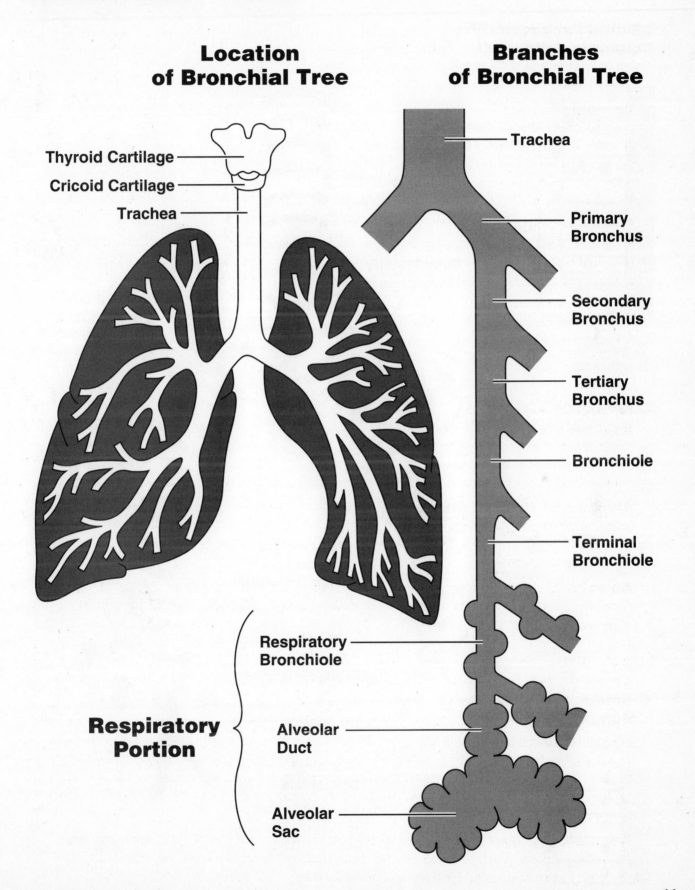

Location
of Bronchial Tree

Thyroid Cartilage

Cricoid Cartilage

Trachea

Respiratory Portion

Respiratory
Bronchiole

Alveolar
Duct

Alveolar
Sac

Branches
of Bronchial Tree

Trachea

Primary
Bronchus

Secondary
Bronchus

Tertiary
Bronchus

Bronchiole

Terminal
Bronchiole

11

BRONCHIAL TREE : Conducting Portion

Ciliated Pseudostratified Columnar Epithelium
lining of the trachea and bronchi

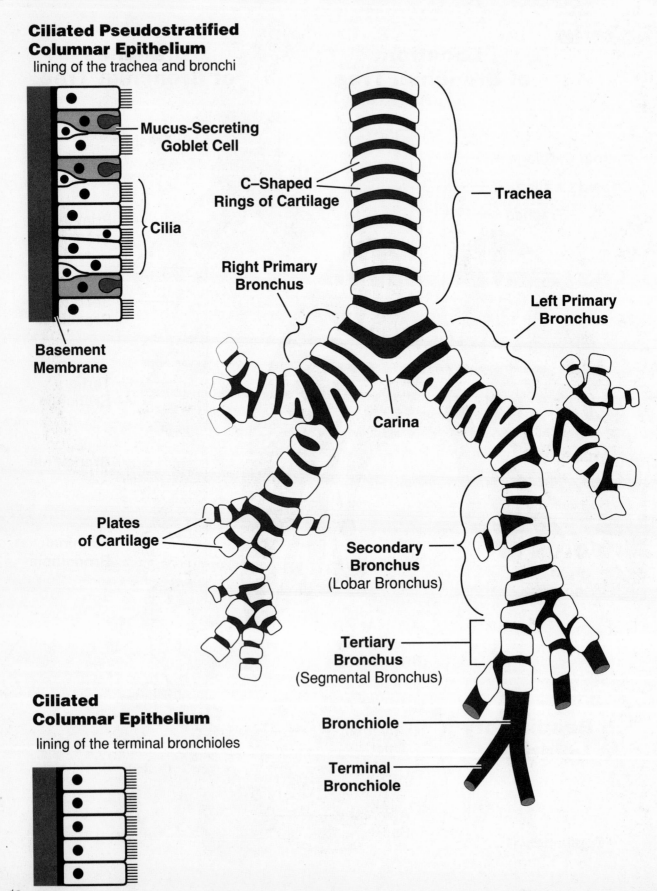

Mucus-Secreting Goblet Cell

Cilia

Basement Membrane

C–Shaped Rings of Cartilage

Trachea

Right Primary Bronchus

Left Primary Bronchus

Carina

Plates of Cartilage

Secondary Bronchus (Lobar Bronchus)

Tertiary Bronchus (Segmental Bronchus)

Bronchiole

Terminal Bronchiole

Ciliated Columnar Epithelium

lining of the terminal bronchioles

BRONCHIAL TREE : Respiratory Portion

Lobule

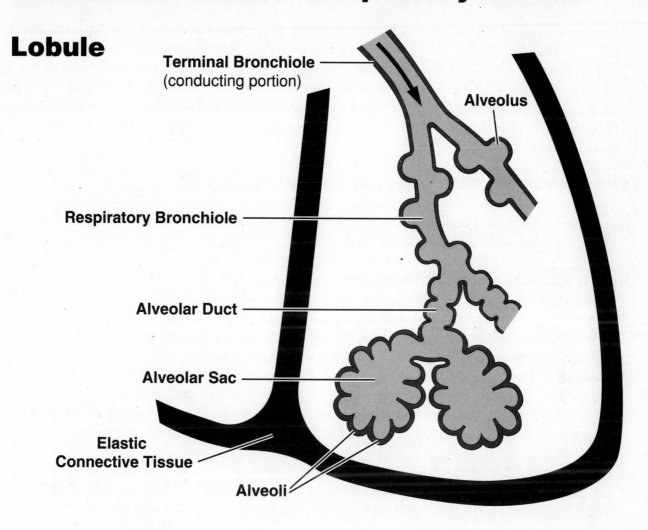

Terminal Bronchiole
(conducting portion)

Alveolus

Respiratory Bronchiole

Alveolar Duct

Alveolar Sac

Elastic
Connective Tissue

Alveoli

Alveolus (Blood Supply)

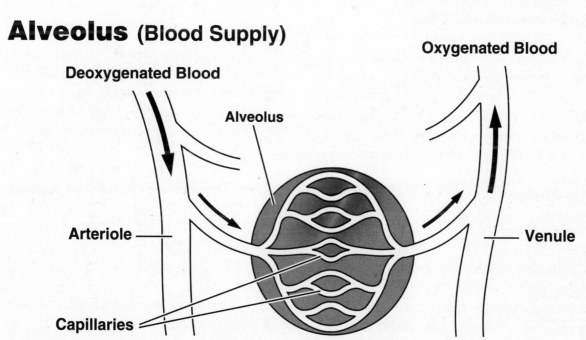

Deoxygenated Blood

Oxygenated Blood

Alveolus

Arteriole

Venule

Capillaries

STRUCTURES / Alveolus

An alveolus (plural: alveoli) is a saclike outpouching of the respiratory portion of the bronchial tree. Most of the alveolar wall (about 97%) consists of very thin squamous epithelial cells called *type I alveolar cells*. The type I cells are interrupted by occasional *type II alveolar cells*, which secrete alveolar fluid. There are about 300 million alveoli in the lungs with a total surface area of about 70 square meters (approximately the size of a tennis court). Alveolar walls, which contain many capillaries, are the only locations where gases are exchanged between the lungs and the blood.

TYPE I ALVEOLAR CELL (Squamous Pulmonary Epithelial Cell)

Type I cells are the very thin (attenuated) squamous epithelial cells that line the walls of alveoli. They are attached by special junctions (desmosomes and occluding junctions) that prevent the leakage of tissue fluid into the alveolar air spaces.

TYPE II ALVEOLAR CELL (Septal Cell)

Type II cells (also called septal cells) are found interspersed among the type I cells. They are secretory cells and have a well-developed Golgi complex and microvilli. When type I and type II cells are destroyed by toxic substances, the remaining type II cells very actively divide, regenerating the alveolar lining.

Surfactant   Type II cells constantly secrete a substance called surfactant, which reduces the surface tension caused by the watery liquid that lines the alveoli. During inspiration, the surfactant reduces the force required to inflate the lungs; during expiration, it prevents the collapse of the alveoli. Surfactant also reduces friction between the air and the tissues.

ALVEOLAR MACROPHAGE (Dust Cell)

Alveolar macrophages (also called dust cells) are found on the surface of the alveolar epithelium within the layer of surfactant. They phagocytize (eat) bacteria and particulate matter.

INTERALVEOLAR SEPTUM

Adjacent alveoli are separated by walls consisting of two very thin squamous epithelial cells; because a single wall forms a partition between two alveoli, it is called a septum. Between the epithelial layers of the septum are fibers (elastic, reticular and collagen), capillaries, fibroblasts, and mast cells. The elastic, reticular, and collagen fibers provide the structural support for the alveoli and give the spongy texture to lung tissue. The capillaries are unusually large, providing more surface area for efficient exchange of gases. Fibroblasts synthesize collagen, reticular fibers, elastic fibers, and intercellular ground substance.

ALVEOLAR–CAPILLARY MEMBRANE (Respiratory Membrane or Blood–Air Barrier)

Four layers separate the blood from the alveolar air:
(1) Type I Alveolar Cells
(2) Epithelial Basement Membrane
(3) Capillary Basement Membrane
(4) Capillary Endothelial Cells
The alveolar-capillary membrane is about 0.5 micrometers thick (a red blood cell has a diameter of about 7 micrometers). This allows rapid diffusion of respiratory gases.

ALVEOLI
Alveoli are found in respiratory bronchioles, alveolar ducts, and alveolar sacs.

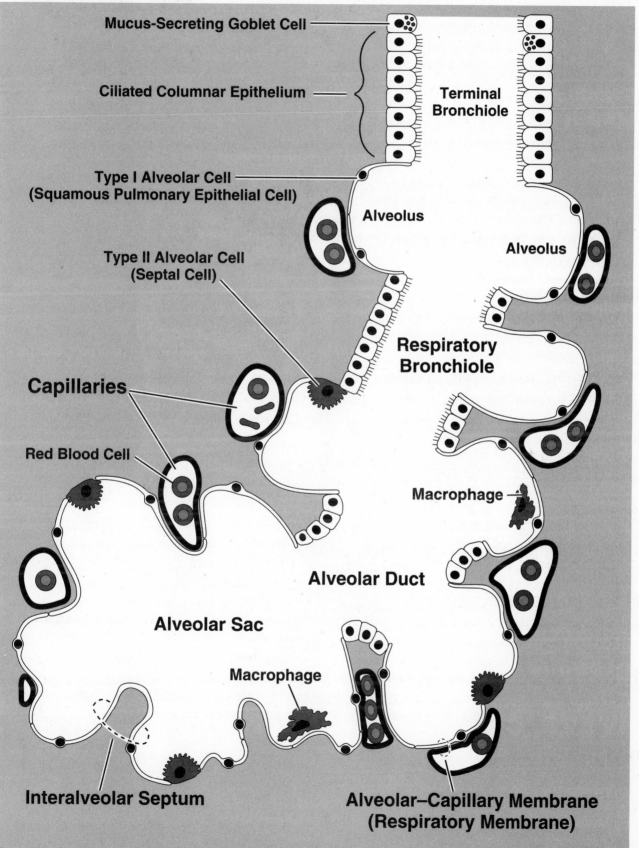

Mucus-Secreting Goblet Cell

Ciliated Columnar Epithelium

Terminal Bronchiole

Type I Alveolar Cell
(Squamous Pulmonary Epithelial Cell)

Alveolus

Alveolus

Type II Alveolar Cell
(Septal Cell)

Respiratory Bronchiole

Capillaries

Red Blood Cell

Macrophage

Alveolar Duct

Alveolar Sac

Macrophage

Interalveolar Septum

Alveolar–Capillary Membrane
(Respiratory Membrane)

STRUCTURES / Lungs

SURFACE ANATOMY

The lungs are paired cone-shaped organs lying in the thoracic cavity. They are separated from each other by the mediastinum (the mass of tissues between the lungs that extends from the sternum to the vertebral column).

Apex (Cupula)   The narrow superior portion of the lung; located one inch above the clavicle.

Base   The concave inferior portion of the lung that fits over the diaphragm.

Hilus   A general term for a depression at the part of an organ where vessels and nerves enter and exit. The region on the medial surface of the lung where the root is attached; where bronchi, pulmonary blood vessels, lymphatic vessels, and nerves enter and exit.

Root   The root is formed by the structures entering and leaving the lung at the hilus.

Cardiac Notch   A concave region on the medial surface of the left lung; where the heart lies.

Fissures   Each lung is divided into lobes by one or more fissures (grooves).

Surfaces   The rounded surface of the lungs lying against the ribs is called the *costal surface*. The surface of the lungs lying against the mediastinum is called the *mediastinal surface* (or *medial surface*).

SUBDIVISIONS

Lobes   The right lung has an *oblique fissure* and a *horizontal fissure*, dividing it into three lobes; the left lung has only an *oblique fissure*, dividing it into two lobes. Each lobe receives its own *secondary (lobar) bronchus*.

Bronchopulmonary Segments   The portion of lung that is supplied by a *tertiary (segmental) bronchus* is called a bronchopulmonary segment. Each segment has a pyramidal shape with it apex facing the root of the lung. There are ten bronchopulmonary segments in the right lung and eight in the left lung.

Lobules   Each bronchopulmonary segment of the lungs is subdivided into many smaller compartments called lobules. Each lobule is wrapped in elastic connective tissue and contains a lymphatic vessel, an arteriole, a venule, and a branch from a *terminal bronchiole*. The terminal bronchioles subdivide into microscopic branches called respiratory bronchioles, which in turn subdivide into several alveolar ducts. Each alveolar duct leads into two or more alveolar sacs, which consist of a cluster of alveoli.

PLEURAL MEMBRANE

There are two layers of serous membrane surrounding each lung, which are collectively called the pleural membrane. Each lung has a pleural membrane.

Parietal Pleura   The outer layer, which is attached to the wall of the thoracic cavity.

Visceral Pleura   The inner layer, which covers the lungs.

Pleural Cavity (Intrapleural Cavity)   The pleural cavity is a small potential space between the parietal and visceral pleurae. It contains a lubricating fluid, which reduces friction.

BLOOD SUPPLY

Oxygenated Blood   Oxygenated blood is delivered to the tissues of the lungs via the bronchial arteries, which branch from the aorta.

Deoxygenated Blood   Deoxygenated blood is delivered to the alveoli via the pulmonary arteries, which branch from the pulmonary trunk.

LUNGS

Location of the Lungs in the Thorax

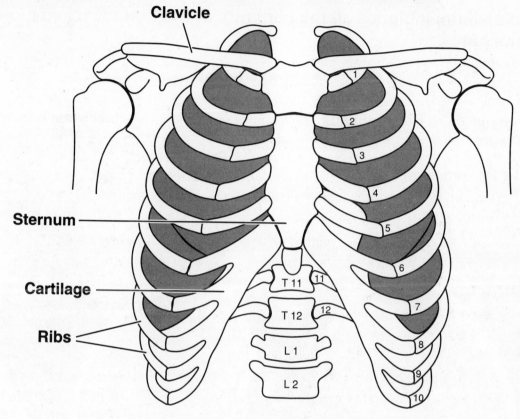

Clavicle

Sternum

Cartilage

Ribs

T 11   11
T 12   12
L 1
L 2

1
2
3
4
5
6
7
8
9
10

Lobes of the Lungs

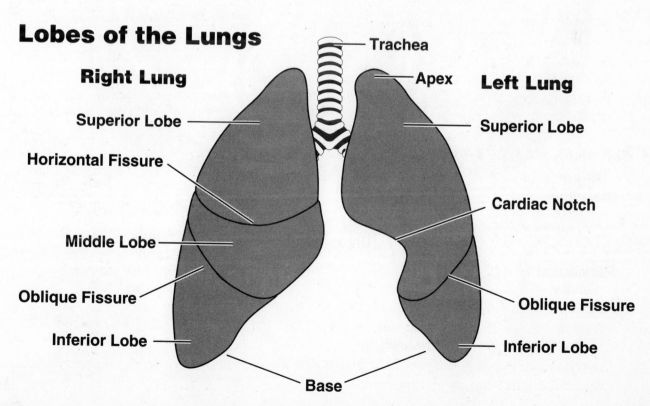

Right Lung

Superior Lobe

Horizontal Fissure

Middle Lobe

Oblique Fissure

Inferior Lobe

Trachea

Apex

Left Lung

Superior Lobe

Cardiac Notch

Oblique Fissure

Inferior Lobe

Base

LUNGS : Transverse Section

Transverse section at the level of the 6th thoracic vertebra.

The mediastinum includes all the contents of the thoracic cavity *except* the lungs.

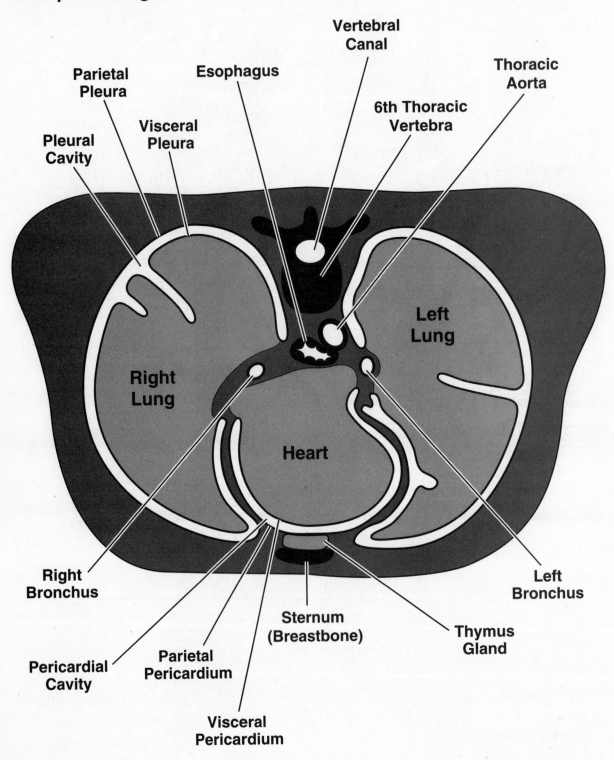

BLOOD SUPPLY TO LUNGS

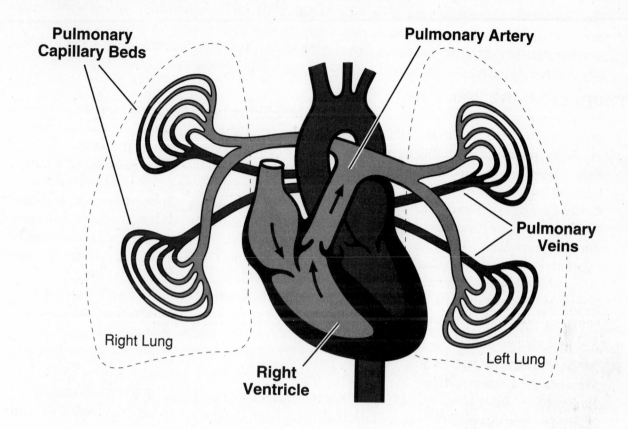

Pulmonary
Capillary Beds

Pulmonary Artery

Pulmonary
Veins

Right
Ventricle

Right Lung

Left Lung

Alveoli and Capillaries

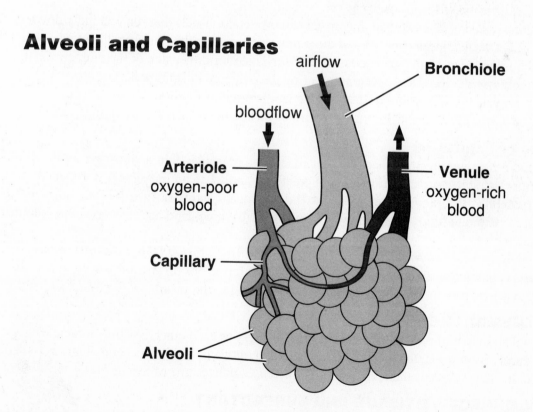

airflow

Bronchiole

bloodflow

Arteriole
oxygen-poor
blood

Venule
oxygen-rich
blood

Capillary

Alveoli

STRUCTURES / Respiratory Pump

The movement of air into and out of the lungs is called pulmonary ventilation. The principal structures involved in this process are the thoracic cage (rib cage), the respiratory muscles, the pleural membranes, and the elastic connective tissue of the lungs. Together these structures act as a respiratory pump, sucking air into the lungs (inspiration) and forcing air out of the lungs (expiration).

THORACIC CAGE (Rib Cage)

The term *thorax* refers to the entire chest. The skeletal portion of the thorax is called the *thoracic cage* or *rib cage*. It is formed by the ribs, costal cartilages, thoracic vertebrae, and sternum. The expanding thoracic cage during inspiration acts like a bellows, sucking air into the lungs.

Ribs   There are 12 pairs of ribs (24 ribs); each rib is attached to a thoracic vertebra. The spaces between the ribs (intercostal spaces) are occupied by intercostal muscles, nerves, and vessels.

Costal Cartilages   The first ten ribs are attached to the sternum by a strip of hyaline cartilage called the costal cartilage (*costa* = rib). The 11th and 12th ribs (floating ribs) do not attach to the sternum.

Thoracic Vertebrae   There are 12 thoracic vertebrae. Each rib has a tubercle (knoblike structure) by which it articulates with the facet (flat surface of a bone that forms part of a joint) of a transverse process on a thoracic vertebra.

Sternum   The sternum is located along the midline in the anterior portion of the rib cage. It is a flat, elongated bone with three parts: the upper portion is the *manubrium*, the middle portion is the *body*, and the lowest portion is the *xiphoid process*.

RESPIRATORY MUSCLES

Muscles of Inspiration

Diaphragm   The diaphragm is the most important muscle of inspiration. It is a dome-shaped skeletal muscle that forms the floor of the thoracic cavity. Contraction causes it to flatten, increasing the vertical dimension of the thoracic cavity.

External Intercostals   The external intercostals are skeletal muscles that run obliquely downward and forward between adjacent ribs. When these muscles contract, the ribs are pulled upward and the sternum is pushed forward; this increases the anterior-posterior dimension of the thoracic cavity.

Sternocleidomastoid   Elevates the sternum during deep, labored inspiration.

Scalenes   Elevate the superior two ribs during deep, labored inspiration.

Pectoralis Minor   Elevates the 3rd through 5th ribs during deep, labored inspiration.

Muscles of Expiration

Expiration during quiet breathing is a passive process (no muscular contractions are involved). Muscles of expiration contract during labored breathing and when air movement is impeded.

Internal Intercostals   Internal intercostals extend downward and backward between adjacent ribs. During forced expiration they contract, which pulls the ribs downward and decreases the volume of the thoracic cavity.

Abdominal Muscles (External Oblique, Rectus Abdominis, Internal Oblique, and Transversus Abdominis)   Contracting abdominal muscles move the inferior ribs downward and compress the abdominal viscera, forcing the diaphragm upward (decreasing the volume of the thoracic cavity).

PLEURAL MEMBRANE

The parietal and visceral pleurae normally adhere strongly to each other. As the thoracic cavity expands during inspiration, the parietal pleura is pulled outward, and the visceral pleura is pulled along with it. This stretches the lung tissue and increases the volume of the air sacs.

ELASTIC CONNECTIVE TISSUE AND SURFACTANT

During quiet breathing, two factors cause the passive expiration of air: (1) the recoil of elastic fibers that were stretched during inspiration and (2) the inward pull of surface tension due to surfactant.

RESPIRATORY MUSCLES
Muscles of Inspiration and Expiration

Muscles of Inspiration

Muscles of Expiration

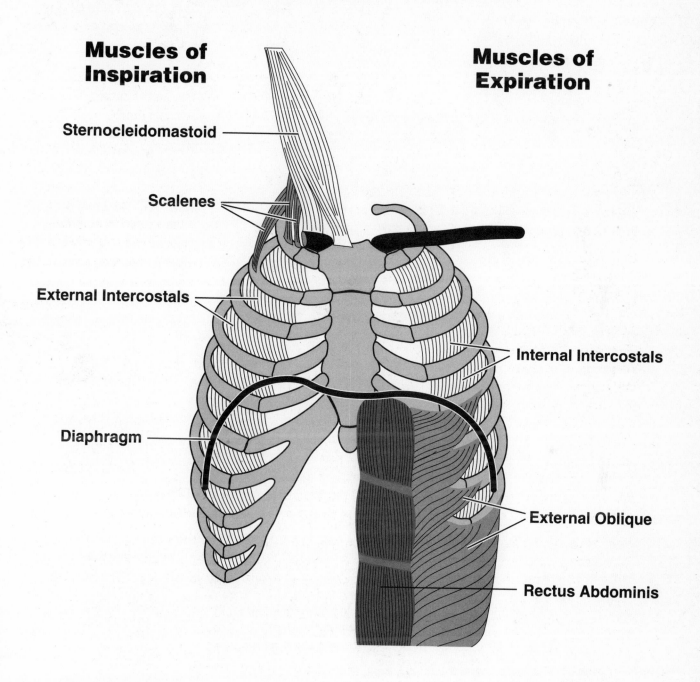

Sternocleidomastoid

Scalenes

External Intercostals

Diaphragm

Internal Intercostals

External Oblique

Rectus Abdominis

Pectoralis Minor

(not illustrated)

**Internal Oblique
and
Transversus Abdominis**

(not illustrated)

2 Ventilation

VENTILATION / Inspiration and Expiration

PRESSURE GRADIENTS

Pulmonary ventilation is the process by which gases are exchanged between the atmosphere and the alveoli of the lungs. Air flows in and out of the lungs for the same reason that blood flows through the blood vessels. All fluids (liquids and gases) move by bulk flow from areas of higher pressure to areas of lower pressure. If the pressure in the atmosphere is greater than the pressure in the alveoli of the lungs, air will flow into the lungs; if the alveolar pressure is greater than the atmospheric pressure, air will flow out of the lungs.

INTRAPLEURAL PRESSURE

Between breaths, when there is no airflow into or out of the lungs, the alveolar pressure is equal to the atmospheric pressure; the pressure in the intrapleural space (between the pleural membranes) is about 4 mm Hg *less than* the atomospheric pressure. Consequently, there is a pressure gradient of about 4 mm Hg pushing the walls of the lungs outward. The intrapleural pressure is always lower than the alveolar pressure; otherwise the lungs would collapse. The magnitude of the pressure gradient varies during breathing, causing the changes in lung size that occur during inspiration and expiration. (Note: Hg is the chemical symbol for mercury.)

INSPIRATION

When the alveolar pressure is less than atmospheric pressure, the pressure gradient causes air to flow into the lungs. The sequence of events is as follows:

(1) Contraction of the diaphragm and inspiratory intercostal muscles (external intercostals). The diaphragm moves downward into the abdomen, enlarging the dimensions of the thoracic cage; the external intercostal muscles pull the ribs upward and outward, enlarging the thoracic cage.

(2) The expanding rib cage pulls the attached pleural membrane outward, enlarging the intrapleural space and, therefore, lowering the intrapleural pressure. This increases the pressure gradient between alveolar and intrapleural spaces, causing the lung wall to be pushed outward.

(3) The lungs expand, increasing the alveolar space and, therefore, lowering the alveolar pressure. The pressure gradient between atmospheric and alveolar air causes the bulk flow of air into the lungs.

EXPIRATION

Expiration is a reversal of the inspiratory process. During expiration, the diaphragm and inspiratory intercostal muscles relax, allowing the elastic lung tissues to recoil. The lungs return to their normal resting size, but because there is additional air in the lungs as the result of inspiration, the resulting alveolar pressure is greater than atmospheric pressure. This pressure gradient favors the bulk flow of air out of the lungs. At rest, expiration is completely passive, requiring no muscular contraction. During exercise, expiratory intercostal muscles (internal intercostals) contract, actively decreasing the thoracic dimensions; also, abdominal muscles contract, increasing intra-abdominal pressure, which increases thoracic pressure by pushing the diaphragm up into the thorax.

LUNG COMPLIANCE

Compliance refers to the ease with which the lungs and thoracic wall can be expanded. A compliant lung is one that is easy to stretch. Lung compliancy is determined by two main factors: tissue structure and surface tension caused by the water lining the inner surfaces of the alveolar walls. A thickening of lung tissue would lead to a lower compliance.

PRESSURE GRADIENTS

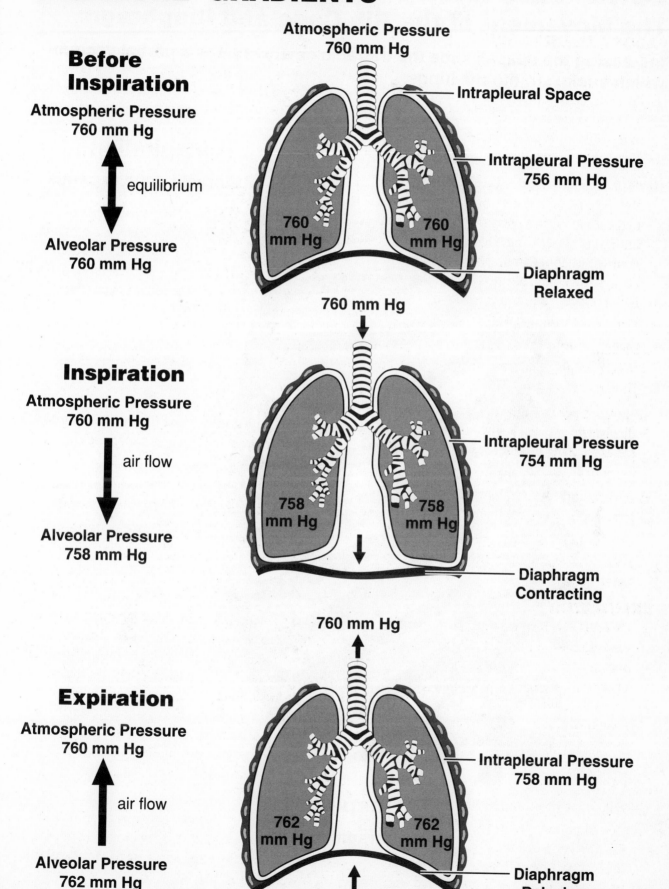

Before Inspiration

Atmospheric Pressure
760 mm Hg

↕ equilibrium

Alveolar Pressure
760 mm Hg

Atmospheric Pressure
760 mm Hg

Intrapleural Space

Intrapleural Pressure
756 mm Hg

760 mm Hg   760 mm Hg

Diaphragm
Relaxed

760 mm Hg

Inspiration

Atmospheric Pressure
760 mm Hg

↓ air flow

Alveolar Pressure
758 mm Hg

Intrapleural Pressure
754 mm Hg

758 mm Hg   758 mm Hg

Diaphragm
Contracting

760 mm Hg

Expiration

Atmospheric Pressure
760 mm Hg

↑ air flow

Alveolar Pressure
762 mm Hg

Intrapleural Pressure
758 mm Hg

762 mm Hg   762 mm Hg

Diaphragm
Relaxing

LUNG VENTILATION
The Movement of the Rib Cage and Diaphragm

Increasing the space inside the thoracic cavity creates a partial vacuum which sucks air into the lungs.

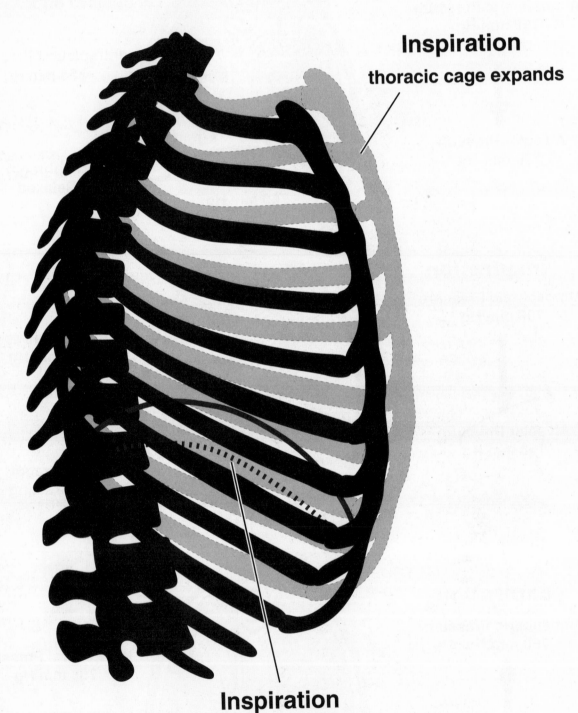

Inspiration
thoracic cage expands

Inspiration
diaphragm lowers

LUNG VENTILATION
The Principal Respiratory Muscles

Inspiration :
the diaphragm contracts and moves downward;
the external intercostals contract, pulling the ribs upward and outward.

Expiration :
the diaphragm relaxes and moves upward;
the internal intercostals contract (only during forced expiration).

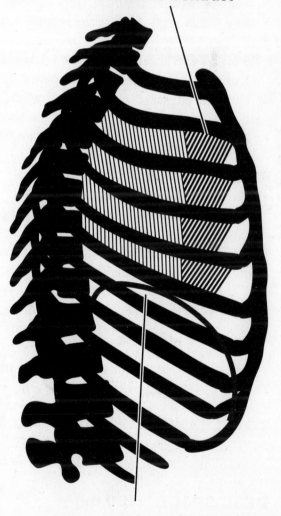

Inspiration
external intercostal
muscles contract

diaphragm lowers

Expiration
internal intercostal
muscles contract

diaphragm bows upward

VENTILATION / Respiratory Volumes

At rest a person inhales about 500 ml (milliliters) of air with each breath and exhales the same amount. The amount of air inhaled can be increased by more forceful contractions of the diaphragm and inspiratory intercostal muscles; the amount of air exhaled can be increased by contraction of the intercostal expiratory muscles (normally expiration is a passive activity resulting from the elastic recoil of the lung tissues). Even after the most forceful exhalation, about 1,200 ml of air remains in the lungs (this prevents collapse of the lungs).

TIDAL VOLUME   (500 ml)

The amount of air that enters the lungs during a normal, quiet inspiration is about 500 ml; it is called the tidal volume. The same volume leaves the lungs during a normal expiration.

INSPIRATORY RESERVE VOLUME   (3,100 ml)

During forced inhalation (a deep breath), the volume of air inspired over and above the tidal volume is called the inspiratory reserve. This volume can be as much as 3,100 ml. The inspiratory reserve can increase the normal tidal volume 6-fold.

EXPIRATORY RESERVE VOLUME   (1,200 ml)

During forced expiration, the volume of air expired over and above the tidal volume is called the expiratory reserve. This volume can be as much as 1,200 ml of air. It requires forceful contractions of the intercostal expiratory muscles (internal intercostals, external oblique, rectus abdominis, internal oblique, and transversus abdominis).

RESIDUAL VOLUME   (1,200 ml)

Even after the most forceful expiration some air remains in the lungs. This is called the residual volume and equals about 1,200 ml. The residual volume prevents the lungs from collapsing. Because residual air remains in the lungs at all times, newly inhaled air is always mixed with air partially depleted of oxygen that is already in the lungs. This prevents the oxygen and carbon dioxide concentrations in the lungs from fluctuating excessively with each breath.

VITAL CAPACITY   (4,800 ml)

The vital capacity is the maximum amount of air a person can exhale after taking the deepest breath possible. It is approximately ten times the volume of air exhaled at rest.

Vital Capacity = Tidal Volume + Inspiratory Reserve + Expiratory Reserve

4,800 ml = 500 ml + 3,100 ml + 1,200 ml

TOTAL LUNG CAPACITY   (6,000 ml)

The *vital capacity* plus the *residual volume* equals the total lung capacity, which is about 6000 ml. This total varies with age, sex, and body size.

DEAD SPACE   (150 ml)

Some of the air that enters the respiratory tract during breathing fails to reach the alveoli. This volume (about 150 ml) remains in the conducting portion of the bronchial tree (trachea, bronchi, and bronchioles). Since gas exchanges do not occur through the walls of these passageways, this air is said to occupy the dead space (nonfunctional for gas exchange).

RESPIRATORY VOLUMES

Inspiratory Reserve Volume = 3,100 ml
Tidal Volume = 500 ml
Expiratory Reserve Volume = 1,200 ml
Residual Volume = 1,200 ml

Vital Capacity = 4,800 ml
Total Lung Volume = 6,000 ml

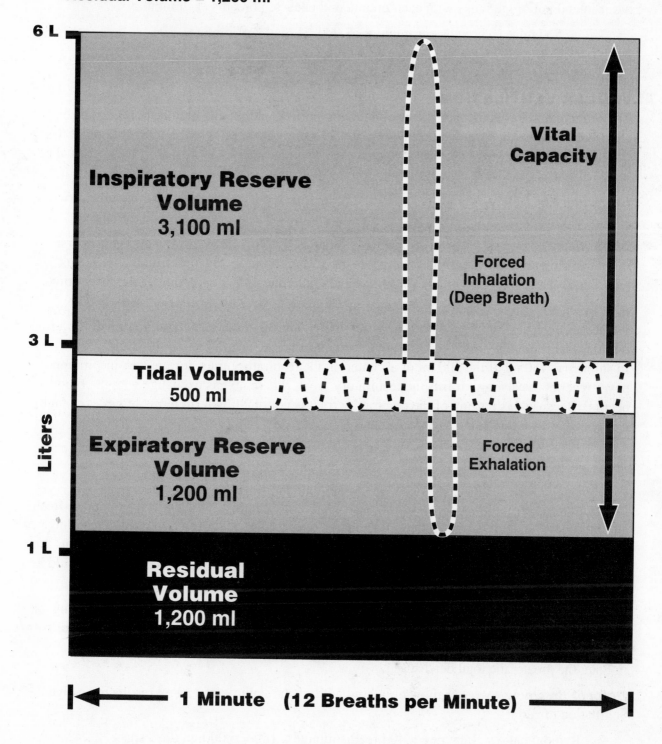

VENTILATION / Alveolar Ventilation

TOTAL PULMONARY VENTILATION

The total pulmonary ventilation per minute is determined by the tidal volume multiplied by the respiratory rate. For example, at rest, a normal person moves approximately 500 ml (milliliters) of air in and out of the lungs with each breath, and takes ten breaths each minute.

500 ml x 10 breaths per minute = 5,000 ml of air per minute

Because of the dead space, not all of this air is available for exchange with the blood.

ALVEOLAR VENTILATION

The bronchial tree is composed of the conducting portion and the respiratory portion. The exchange of gases with the blood occurs only in the respiratory portion. The total volume of the conducting portion, where no exchange occurs, is approximately 150 ml. This volume is called the dead space, because it is nonfunctional in terms of gas exchange.

Expiration #1   During expiration, 500 ml of air is forced out of the alveoli through the airways; 350 ml of this air is exhaled; 150 ml still remains in the airways at the end of expiration.

Inspiration #1   During the next inspiration, 500 ml of air flows into the alveoli, but the first 150 ml of entering air is not atmospheric air; it is the 150 ml of air left behind from the previous expiration. Thus, only 350 ml of *new* atmospheric air enters the alveoli during the inspiration.

Expiration #2   At the end of inspiration, 150 ml of fresh air also fills the conducting airways, but no gas exchange with the blood can occur there. During the next expiration, this fresh air will be washed out and again replaced by old alveolar air, thus completing the cycle.
In summary, 150 ml of the 500 ml of air entering the respiratory tract during each inspiration never reaches the alveoli. It fills the respiratory tubes, where no gas exchange with the blood occurs. Because this portion of the respiratory tract is nonfunctional (in terms of gas exchange) it is called the *anatomic dead space*.

Tidal Volume = 500 ml
Dead Space = 150 ml
Fresh air entering alveoli = 350 ml

Calculation of the Alveolar Ventilation   Alveolar ventilation is defined as the volume of fresh air entering the alveoli *each minute*. To calculate the alveolar ventilation, multiply the volume of fresh air entering the alveoli during a single inspiration times the breathing frequency. If an individual breathes ten times per minute, the alveolar ventilation of the above example would be 10 x 350 ml = 3,500 ml.

Rate of Breathing   The alveolar ventilation is inversely proportional to the rate of breathing; as a person breathes more rapidly, the depth of breathing and the alveolar ventialtion decrease. This is because each inspiration includes 150 ml of dead space; thus, the more breaths per minute, the greater the total dead space.

Depth of Breathing   Very shallow breathing with a tidal volume of 150 ml results in an alveolar ventilation of *zero*.

Rapid, Shallow Breathing : 40 breaths/minute x 150 = 6,000 ml dead space
Normal Breathing : 12 breaths/minute x 150 = 1,800 ml dead space
Slow, Deep Breathing : 6 breaths/minute x 150 = 900 ml dead space

ALVEOLAR VENTILATION

Dead Space

The dead space is the region of the respiratory tract where no gas exchange occurs.
It is approximately 150 ml of nonfunctional space.

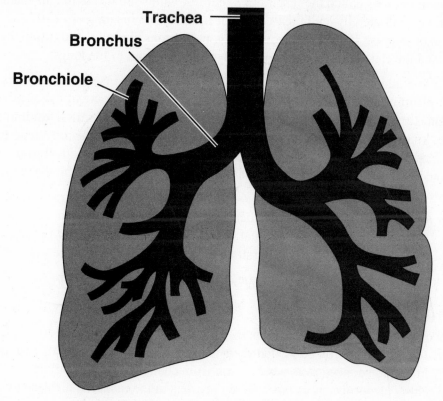

Respiratory Portion

Gas exchange occurs only in the respiratory portion, where alveoli are present.
The respiratory portion includes:
respiratory bronchioles, alveolar ducts, and alveolar sacs.

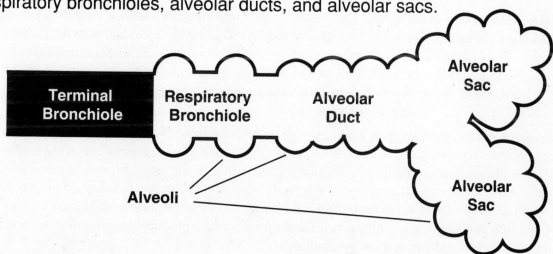

NERVOUS CONTROL

Inspiratory Neurons in the Medulla

The diaphragm and the intercostal muscles control ventilation. They are skeletal muscles and cannot contract unless stimulated by nerves. The motor neurons that innervate these inspiratory muscles are regulated by a group of neurons called the inspiratory neurons, which are located in the medulla oblongata. Inspiration is initiated by an increased rate of firing by the inspiratory neurons and the recruitment of new motor units. Expiration begins when the neurons abruptly stop firing, the inspiratory muscles relax, and the elastic lungs recoil, passively forcing air out of the lungs.

Rhythm Rhythmical breathing depends on the cyclical excitation of the inspiratory muscles. The mechanism for this on-off cycle is unclear. It has been hypothesized that some of the inspiratory neurons act as pacemaker cells, discharging automatically at a fixed inherent rate. Besides the pathways leading down toward the respiratory muscles, there may be interconnecting neurons forming loops that feed back on the pacemaker cells. Fast, positive-feedback loops (reflex arcs) cause the initial rapid buildup of discharge; slower, negative-feedback loops inhibit the pacemaker cells and abruptly stop the firing of impulses.

Pulmonary Stretch Receptors Stretch receptors located in the walls of airways are activated by deep breathing (they have a high threshold); unusual lung inflation stimulates these receptors, which send impulses to the medulla and inhibit the inspiratory neurons.

Pons Input from areas in the pons also modifies the output of the inspiratory neurons.

CHEMICAL CONTROL

Involuntary control of ventilation is regulated primarily by input from chemoreceptors. The peripheral chemoreceptors (carotid and aortic bodies) are sensitive to low levels of blood oxygen and changes in blood hydrogen ion concentrations that result from changes in blood carbon dioxide concentrations; the central chemoreceptors (specialized neurons in the medulla) are sensitive to changes in the hydrogen ion concentration of the interstitial fluid in the brain.

Oxygen (receptors: peripheral chemoreceptors, especially the carotid bodies) When the arterial partial pressure of oxygen drops below 60 mm Hg, there is a marked increase in ventilation. At 60 mm Hg the hemoglobin molecules in red blood cells are nearly 90% saturated, so oxygen transport is still sufficient. Below 60 mm Hg, hemoglobin saturation drops precipitously, so the oxygen-carrying capacity of blood is markedly reduced.

Carbon Dioxide (receptors: central chemoreceptors) An increase in arterial carbon dioxide concentration results in an increase in the formation of carbonic acid (water combines with the carbon dioxide). The carbonic acid dissociates, forming hydrogen ions and bicarbonate ions. These are called carbon dioxide-dependent hydrogen ions, and they are monitored by the central chemoreceptors in the medulla. Increased hydrogen ion concentration stimulates increased ventilation. Below normal hydrogen ion concentrations inhibit ventilation.

Hydrogen Ion Concentration (receptors: peripheral chemoreceptors) Changes in hydrogen ion concentration that are not due to changes in the arterial carbon dioxide concentration are monitored by the peripheral chemoreceptors. An increase in the hydrogen ion concentration resulting from accumulation of lactic acid during exercise induces hyperventilation, which increases the rate of excretion of carbon dioxide and thus lowers arterial levels of carbon dioxide and hydrogen ions. A decrease in hydrogen ion concentrations resulting from vomiting induces hypoventilation, which has the opposite effect on hydrogen ion concentration.

BREATHING : Nervous Control

Central Chemoreceptors

stimulated by
high carbon dioxide

Carotid Bodies

stimulated by
low oxygen

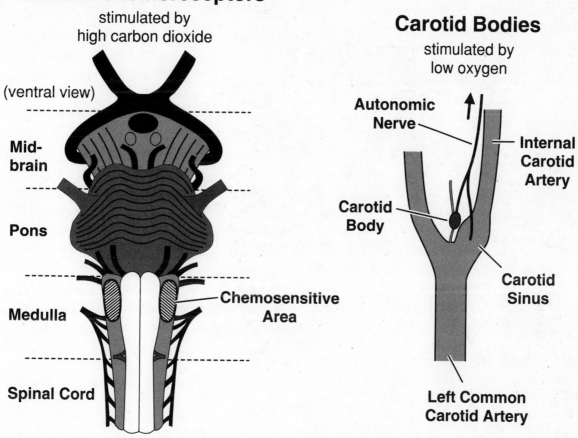

(ventral view)

Mid-
brain

Pons

Medulla

Spinal Cord

Chemosensitive
Area

Autonomic
Nerve

Internal
Carotid
Artery

Carotid
Body

Carotid
Sinus

Left Common
Carotid Artery

Respiratory Centers in the Brainstem

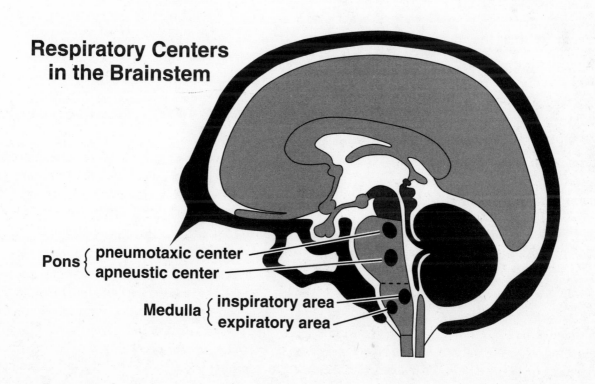

Pons { pneumotaxic center
apneustic center

Medulla { inspiratory area
expiratory area

3 Gas Exchange and Transport

GAS EXCHANGE AND TRANSPORT / Overview

The exchange of gases between the atmospheric air, blood, and cells is called respiration. The purpose of respiration is twofold: (1) to get oxygen from the air into the mitochondria of tissue cells; and (2) to get carbon dioxide produced from cellular activities out of the body. The following outline describes the basic processes involved.

INSPIRATION (First Phase of Pulmonary Ventilation)

During inspiration, an expanded rib cage causes a decrease in the pressure inside the lungs, which results in the bulk flow of atmospheric air into the lungs. In the air sacs of the lungs (alveoli) the oxygen-rich air comes into close contact with pulmonary capillaries.

EXTERNAL RESPIRATION (Pulmonary Respiration)

External respiration (pulmonary respiration) is the exchange of gases between the lungs and blood. The partial pressure (concentration) of oxygen is greater in the alveolar gases than in the blood plasma, so the concentration gradient favors the diffusion of oxygen from the alveoli into the blood capillaries across the *alveolar-capillary membrane*. The opposite is true for carbon dioxide: the partial pressure (concentration) of carbon dioxide is greater in the blood plasma than in the alveolar air, so carbon dioxide diffuses from the blood plasma into the alveoli.

OXYGEN TRANSPORT

Once in the blood plasma, oxygen diffuses into the red blood cells and combines with the iron atoms in hemoglobin molecules. About 98.5% of the oxygen molecules are transported in the blood combined with hemoglobin; only 1.5% of the oxygen dissolves in the blood plasma.

INTERNAL RESPIRATION (Tissue Respiration)

Internal respiration (tissue respiration) is the exchange of gases between the blood and the cells. The partial pressure (concentration) of oxygen is greater in the blood than in the tissue fluids. So, as blood passes through the capillaries of tissues, some oxygen, which is released by the hemoglobin, diffuses from the blood into the tissue fluids and into the cells. Carbon dioxide, produced by cellular respiration, is more concentrated in the tissue fluids than in the blood, so it diffuses into the blood.

CARBON DIOXIDE TRANSPORT

Most of the carbon dioxide in the blood diffuses into red blood cells and is combined with water to form carbonic acid (H_2CO_3). The carbonic acid dissociates into *hydrogen ions* (which combine with hemoglobin) and *bicarbonate ions* (HCO_3^-), which diffuse out of the red blood cells into the plasma. About 70% of the carbon dioxide is transported as bicarbonate ions dissolved in the blood plasma. About 23% of the carbon dioxide molecules combine with hemoglobin, and about 7% of the carbon dioxide molecules are dissolved in the blood plasma.

EXPIRATION (Second Phase of Pulmonary Ventilation)

In the pulmonary capillaries, the chemical reactions that formed bicarbonate ions in the tissue capillaries reverse, forming carbon dioxide, which diffuses from the blood into the alveoli (air sacs). During expiration, the decreased size of the thoracic cavity increases the pressure inside the lungs, which results in the bulk flow of air rich in carbon dioxide out of the lungs.

GAS EXCHANGE OVERVIEW

External (Pulmonary) Respiration

The exchange of gases between alveoli and blood capillaries.

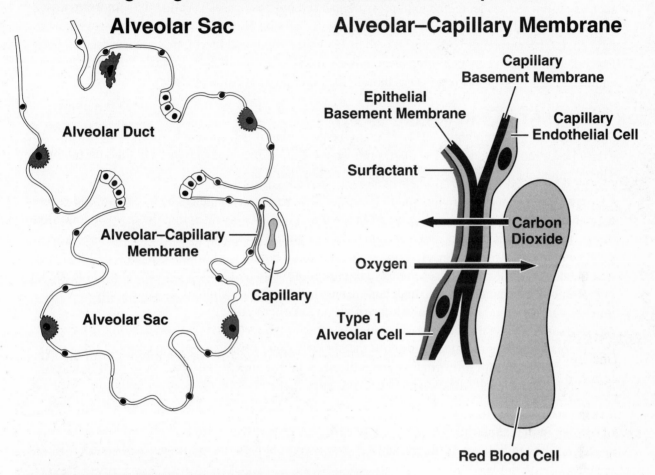

Alveolar Sac

- Alveolar Duct
- Alveolar–Capillary Membrane
- Capillary
- Alveolar Sac

Alveolar–Capillary Membrane

- Capillary Basement Membrane
- Epithelial Basement Membrane
- Capillary Endothelial Cell
- Surfactant
- Carbon Dioxide
- Oxygen
- Type 1 Alveolar Cell
- Red Blood Cell

Internal (Tissue) Respiration

The exchange of gases between blood capillaries and tissue cells.

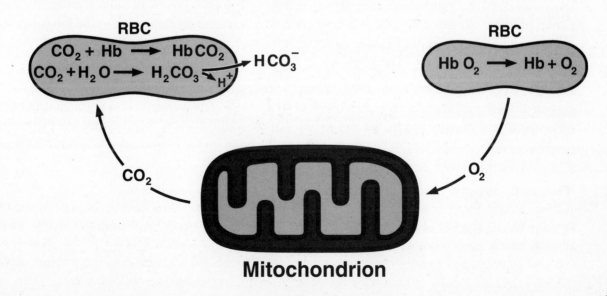

RBC

$$CO_2 + Hb \longrightarrow HbCO_2$$
$$CO_2 + H_2O \longrightarrow H_2CO_3 \searrow H^+$$
$$\longrightarrow HCO_3^-$$

RBC

$$HbO_2 \longrightarrow Hb + O_2$$

CO_2

O_2

Mitochondrion

GAS EXCHANGE AND TRANSPORT / Partial Pressures

ATMOSPHERIC PRESSURE

Atmospheric air is a mixture of gases: nitrogen, oxygen, carbon dioxide, water vapor, and inert gases such as argon. At sea level, the total pressure exerted by these gases is called the atmospheric pressure (also called barometric pressure); it equals 760 mm Hg. Air is about 79% nitrogen, 21% oxygen, 0.04% carbon dioxide, and less than 1% water vapor and inert gases such as argon. These gas molecules are in constant movement and are so far apart that they have little influence on one another. Each type of gas behaves as though the other gases were not present.

OXYGEN PARTIAL PRESSURE (pO_2)

Since oxygen makes up about 21% of the molecules in air, it is responsible for 21% of the pressure exerted by atmospheric air: 21% of 760 mm Hg = 0.21 x 760 = 159.6 mm Hg (about 160 mm Hg) This is called the partial pressure of oxygen in atmospheric air.

Lungs With every inspiration about 350 ml of new air enters the lungs by bulk flow and mixes with about 2500 ml of air already present in the the lungs. The result is that the oxygen concentration of the new air is diluted, and, consequently, the partial pressure of oxygen in the alveoli is reduced to about 105 mm Hg. Alveolar partial pressure remains relatively constant. During inspiration the new volume of air raises the oxygen partial pressure and lowers the carbon dioxide partial pressure; but the change is very small and insignificant since the volume of new air entering the lungs is very small relative to the volume of air already in the lungs.

Net Diffusion The difference in the partial pressures (concentrations) of oxygen on the two sides of the alveolar-capillary membrane result in the net diffusion of oxygen into the blood. Oxygen diffuses down its concentration gradient from the alveoli (105 mm Hg) to the blood (40 mm Hg) until equilibrium is achieved (the oxygen partial pressure in the alveolar air is equal to that in the blood).

Tissues As the blood passes through the tissues the reverse process occurs. The partial pressure of oxygen in the tissue fluids is about 40 mm Hg. Oxygen diffuses from the blood into the tissue spaces until equilibrium is achieved and the oxygen partial pressures in tissue fluids and the blood are equal to 40 mm Hg.

CARBON DIOXIDE PARTIAL PRESSURE (pCO_2)

Since carbon dioxide makes up only 0.04% of the molecules in air, it is responsible for 0.04 % of the pressure exerted by atmospheric air : 0.04% of 760 = 0.0004 x 760 = 0.3 mm Hg. This is the partial pressure of carbon dioxide in atmospheric air. Since the air remaining in the lungs between breaths is high in carbon dioxide, the carbon dioxide partial pressure in the lungs is higher than in atmospheric air; it is about 40 mm Hg.

Lungs As blood enters the lungs the carbon dioxide partial pressure is 45 mm Hg, while the carbon dioxide partial pressure in the alveoli is 40 mm Hg. The concentration gradient causes the net diffusion of carbon dioxide into the alveoli. Complete equilibrium is usually achieved by the time the blood leaves a capillary, so blood returning to the heart in the pulmonary veins has a carbon dioxide partial pressure of 40 mm Hg.

Tissues In active tissue cells the carbon dioxide partial pressure is about 45 mm Hg. As blood passes through tissue capillaries, there is a net diffusion of carbon dioxide from the interstitial fluid into the blood; equilibrium is achieved and the blood returning to the heart from tissues has a carbon dioxide partial pressure of 45 mm Hg.

PARTIAL PRESSURES

Approximately 21% of the molecules in the air are oxygen molecules.
21% of atmospheric pressure is : 0.21 x 760 mm Hg = 160 mm Hg

atmospheric P O$_2$ = 160 mm Hg

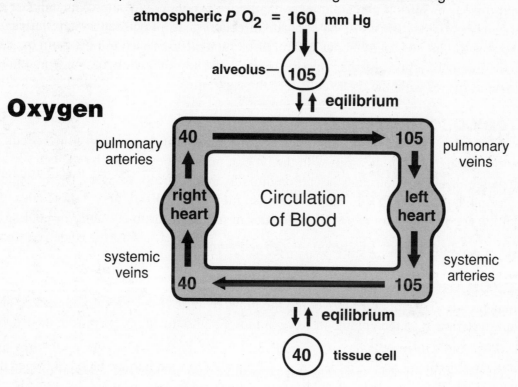

Oxygen

atmospheric P CO$_2$ = 0.3 mm Hg

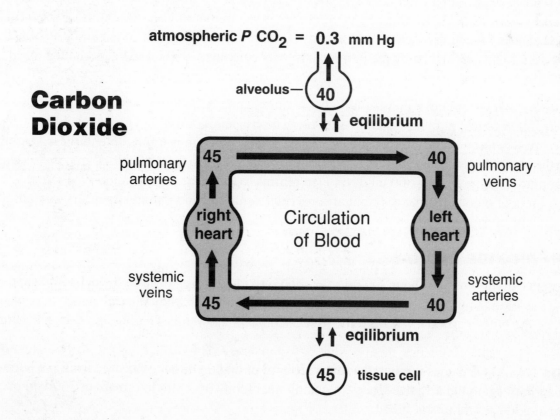

Carbon Dioxide

Gas exchange occurs in two locations: the lungs and the tissues. In the the lungs, about 200 ml of oxygen diffuse from alveoli into pulmonary capillaries every minute; approximately the same amount of carbon dioxide diffuses in the opposite direction — from pulmonary capillaries into the alveolar spaces. In the tissues, about 200 ml of oxygen diffuses each minute from the capillaries into the interstitial fluid and then into the tissue cells; approximately the same amount of carbon dioxide diffuses from the tissue cells into the capillaries.

RESPIRATORY QUOTIENT (RQ)

The amount of carbon dioxide produced divided by the amount of oxygen consumed is equal to the respiratory quotient (RQ). It varies with the type of nutrient being used by the cell. When glucose is metabolized, 10 molecules of carbon dioxide are produced for every 10 molecules of oxygen consumed; glucose RQ = 1. However, when fat is metabolized, only 7 molecules of carbon dioxide are produced for every 10 molecules of oxygen consumed; fat RQ = 0.7.

RQ = carbon dioxide produced ÷ oxygen consumed

OXYGEN EXCHANGE   (At rest, assuming the RQ = 1)

Every minute about 5,000 ml of air move into the lungs by bulk flow. Oxygen makes up about 21% of atmospheric air, so the volume of oxygen moving into the lungs every minute is 21% of 5,000 ml (about 1,000 ml).

Lungs   Of the 1,000 ml of oxygen that enter the lungs each minute only 200 ml diffuse across the alveolar walls into the pulmonary capillaries; the remaining 800 ml of oxygen is exhaled. The 200 ml of oxygen that enter the capillaries is absorbed by 5 liters of blood — the amount of blood that passes through the lungs every minute (cardiac output = 5 liters / minute). The 5 liters of blood entering the lungs each minute already contains about 800 ml of oxygen, so the blood carried back to the left atrium by the pulmonary veins contains 1,000 ml oxygen / 5 liters of blood.

Tissues   Every minute, 5 liters of blood containing about 1,000 ml of oxygen is pumped from the left ventricle into the systemic arteries. The concentration of oxygen remains constant as blood passes through the arteries and arterioles, since exchange is impossible in these vessels. When the blood reaches the capillaries, 200 ml of oxygen diffuse from the blood into the tissues each minute. The remaining 800 ml of oxygen returns to the heart via the veins. Therefore, every 5 liters of blood entering the right atrium, right ventricle, and pulmonary artery contain about 800 ml of oxygen.

CARBON DIOXIDE EXCHANGE

Tissues   Every minute about 200 ml of carbon dioxide diffuses from tissue cells into capillaries. The blood in the capillaries already contains 2,600 ml of carbon dioxide per 5 liters of blood, so the blood carried away from the tissues contains 2,800 ml of carbon dioxide per 5 liters of blood.

Lungs   As blood passes through the lungs, 200 ml of carbon dioxide diffuses from the pulmonary capillaries into the alveolar spaces, reducing the blood concentration to about 2600 ml of carbon dioxide per 5 liters of blood.

GAS EXCHANGE

Every minute 200 ml of oxygen are absorbed by the blood plasma and 200 ml of carbon dioxide are released from the blood plasma.

Oxygen

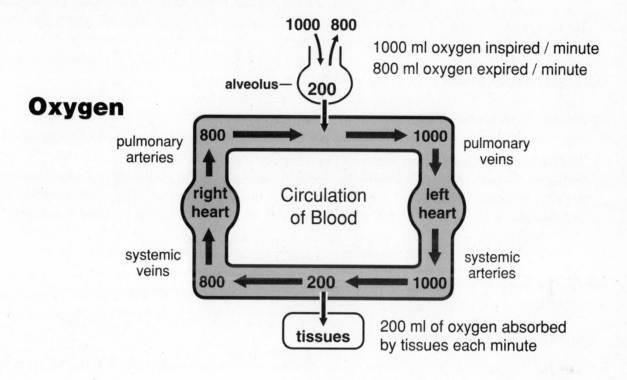

1000 ml oxygen inspired / minute
800 ml oxygen expired / minute

200 ml of oxygen absorbed by tissues each minute

Carbon Dioxide

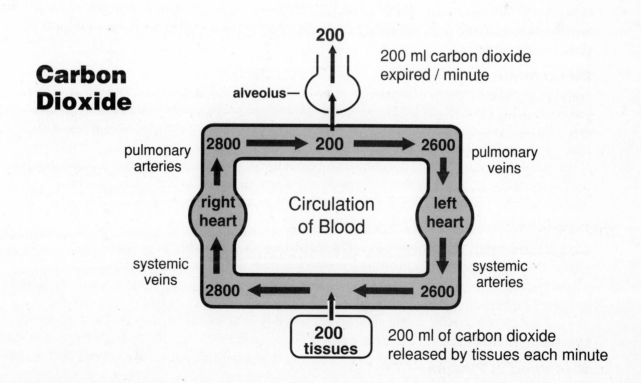

200 ml carbon dioxide expired / minute

200 ml of carbon dioxide released by tissues each minute

Most oxygen molecules are transported in red blood cells chemically combined with hemoglobin. About 23% of the carbon dioxide transported by the blood is also combined with hemoglobin, but the greatest number of carbon dioxide molecules (about 70%) are dissolved in the blood plasma in the form of the bicarbonate ion (HCO_3^-).

OXYGEN TRANSPORT

Each minute 1,000 ml of oxygen are transported by the blood from the lungs to the tissues. The cardiac output is about 5 liters per minute. Therefore, each minute 5 liters of blood transports 1,000 ml of oxygen (1 liter of blood transports 200 ml of oxygen).

Combined with Hemoglobin (Oxyhemoglobin) — 98.5%

About 98.5% of the oxygen carried in the blood is combined with hemoglobin. The reaction between hemoglobin and oxygen forms oxyhemoglobin and is reversible. The extent to which hemoglobin combines with oxygen depends primarily on the oxygen partial pressure (concentration) in the plasma.

In the lung capillaries there is a relatively high oxygen partial pressure, so more oxygen diffuses into the red blood cells and combines with hemoglobin. A relatively low oxygen partial pressure in the tissue capillaries causes the release of oxygen from hemoglobin in the tissue capillaries.

Dissolved in Plasma Water — 1.5%

The remaining 1.5% of the oxygen transported by the blood is dissolved in the water of the plasma (oxygen is relatively insoluble in water).

CARBON DIOXIDE TRANSPORT

Most of the carbon dioxide released from active tissue cells diffuses into the blood plasma and then into the red blood cells. In the red blood cells some of the carbon dioxide combines with water to form carbonic acid, and some carbon dioxide combines with hemoglobin to form carbaminohemoglobin.

Bicarbonate Ions — 70%

About 70% of the carbon dioxide is transported in the plasma as bicarbonate ions.

Carbonic Anhydrase   Red blood cells contain an enzyme called carbonic anhydrase that catalyzes the reaction between carbon dioxide and water. The resulting carbonic acid dissociates, releasing hydrogen ions and bicarbonate ions.

Most of the hydrogen ions combine with hemoglobin, which acts as a buffer (keeping the pH relatively constant). The bicarbonate ions diffuse out of the red blood cells into the blood plasma, which carries the bicarbonate ions to the lungs. In the lungs the process is reversed, releasing carbon dioxide, which diffuses into the alveoli.

Combined with Hemoglobin (Carbaminohemoglobin) — 23%

About 23% of the carbon dioxide is transported as carbaminohemoglobin. Carbon dioxide combines with hemoglobin, but not with the iron atoms; carbon dioxide combines with the amino groups of the protein portion of hemoglobin, forming carbaminohemoglobin. Consequently, oxygen and carbon dioxide do not compete for bonding sites, and both gases can be transported by a hemoglobin molecule at the same time.

Dissolved in Plasma — 7%

About 7% of the carbon dioxide tranported by the blood is dissolved in the water of the plasma. Carbon dioxide is more soluble in water than oxygen.

GAS TRANSPORT

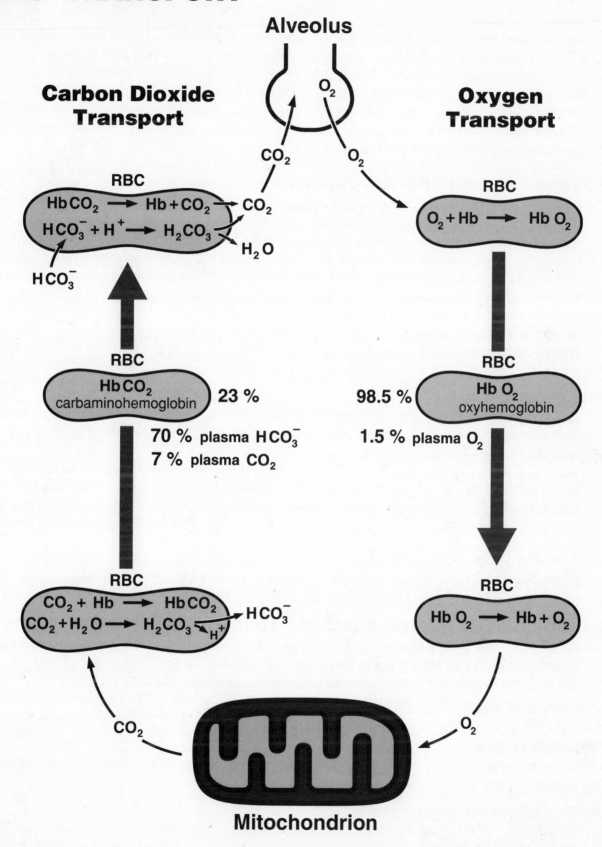

43

Hemoglobin (Hb)   Hemoglobin is a protein composed of 4 polypeptide chains, each of which contains a single atom of iron. It is with the iron atom that a molecule of oxygen combines; thus, each hemoglobin molecule can combine with 4 molecules of oxygen. When all of the iron atoms in a group of hemoglobin molecules are combined with oxygen, the hemoglobin is said to be fully (100%) saturated.

Oxygen-Hemoglobin Dissociation Curve   An oxygen-hemoglobin dissociation (or saturation) curve shows the quantitative relationship between oxygen saturation and a variable such as temperature, pH, or plasma partial pressure (concentration).

OXYGEN PARTIAL PRESSURE (pO_2)

By far the most important factor controlling the oxygen saturation of hemoglobin is the partial pressure of oxygen in the blood plasma (the concentration of dissolved oxygen). Raising the concentration of plasma oxygen increases the diffusion of oxygen into the red blood cells, which results in more binding of oxygen with hemoglobin. The extent to which hemoglobin combines with oxygen increases very rapidly from 10 to 60 mm Hg. When the partial pressure of oxygen in the plasma is 60 mm Hg, the hemoglobin is 90% saturated. This means that even if the partial pressure of oxygen drops from its normal value of 100% down to 60%, the quantity of oxygen carried by the hemoglobin would decrease by only 10%. This provides a safety factor that guarantees a constant supply of oxygen to the tissues. For this reason, certain respiratory and circulatory diseases that result in a lower alveolar ventilation do not have a significant effect on the delivery of oxygen to the tissues.

THE BOHR EFFECT

As acidity increases (pH decreases), hemoglobin (Hb) releases oxygen more readily; this is called the Bohr effect. Hydrogen ions exert this effect by combining with hemoglobin and altering its molecular structure.

Tissue Capillaries   The hydrogen ion concentration in tissue capillaries is greater than in arterial blood; so blood flowing through tissue capillaries becomes more acidic, enhancing release of oxygen.

Lung Capillaries   The hydrogen ion concentration in lung capillaries is lower than in the systemic venous blood; so blood flowing through the lungs becomes less acidic, which enhances the combining of oxygen with hemoglobin.

Active Tissue   The more active a tissue, the greater the hydrogen ion concentration, since high concentrations of metabolic carbon dioxide form carbonic acid. As a result, the release of oxygen from hemoglobin is enhanced as the blood flows through active tissue capillaries.

CARBON DIOXIDE PARTIAL PRESSURE (pCO_2)

As the pCO_2 increases, hemoglobin releases oxygen (O_2) more readily. The partial pressure of carbon dioxide and the acidity (pH) of the blood are closely related.

Carbonic Anhydrase   As carbon dioxide is taken up by the blood, much of it is converted into carbonic acid; this reaction is catalyzed by the enzyme carbonic anhydrase, which is present inside red blood cells.

TEMPERATURE

As the temperature increases, hemoglobin releases oxygen more readily. Active cells require more oxygen and release more heat as a by-product of metabolic activity.

BPG (2,3-biphosphoglycerate)

As the level of BPG increases, hemoglobin releases oxygen more readily. BPG is a substance formed in red blood cells during glycolysis. It binds reversibly with hemoglobin, causing it to have a lower affinity for oxygen. Glycolysis (and BPG production) increases when there is an insufficient oxygen supply to the tissues. (Note: BPG was previously called DPG or diphosphoglycerate.)

HEMOGLOBIN SATURATION

As plasma oxygen increases,
Hb saturation increases.

In venous blood,
$p\,O_2$ is 40 mm Hg and
Hb is 75% saturated.

In arterial blood,
$p\,O_2$ is 105 mm Hg and
Hb is 98% saturated.

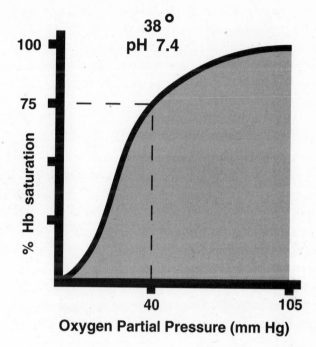

Effect of pH

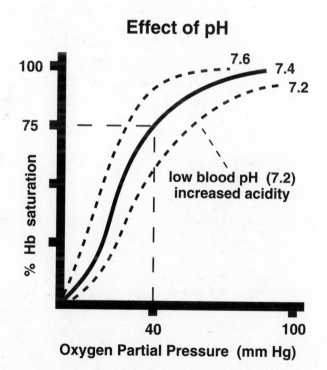

As acidity increases,
less oxygen combines with Hb

Effect of Temperature

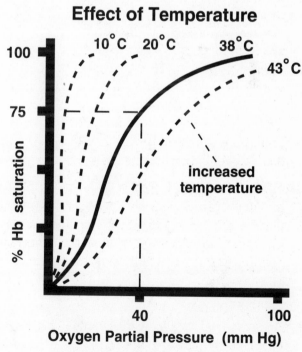

As temperature increases,
less oxygen combines with Hb

4 Cellular Respiration

CELLULAR RESPIRATION / Overview

THE FATE OF OXYGEN

The purpose of breathing is to get oxygen into the blood, and, ultimately, into the mitochondria of individual cells. Oxygen is required for the "burning" of glucose just as it is required for the burning of wood. When a fuel is burned, the carbon–hydrogen bonds of the fuel molecules are broken and energy is released. When wood or natural gas is burned, the energy released is in the form of heat, which dissipates into the environment.

When glucose is burned (oxidized) in the mitochondria of cells, 60% of the energy released is in the form of heat; 40% is transferred to another chemical—ATP (adenosine triphosphate). ATP stores energy in a form that is immediately usable for cell functions.

FUELS

The functioning of a cell depends upon its ability to extract the chemical energy locked in the carbon–hydrogen bonds of organic molecules. Carbohydrates and lipids (fats) are the main sources of energy (fuels) for cells. After a meal, when glucose is being absorbed by the digestive tract, it is the main fuel used by cells to produce ATP. Between meals, when glucose is not being absorbed into the blood, fats stored in adipose tissue are released into the blood and used for the production of ATP. During starvation, muscle proteins also can be broken down for energy use.

ATP

ATP is a large molecule that consists of a nitrogenous base (adenine), a five-carbon sugar (ribose), and three phosphate groups linked in tandem. The three phosphate groups are linked by two high-energy bonds; when these bonds are broken (hydrolysis of ATP), a relatively large amount of energy is released. It is the principal form of energy used by cells to carry out their energy-requiring functions, such as the movement of cilia, the contraction of muscle cells, the active transport of molecules across a cell membrane, and the synthesis of organic molecules.

Energy is continuously cycled through ATP molecules. A typical ATP molecule may exist for only a few seconds before it is broken down into ADP (adenosine diphosphate) and inorganic phosphate. ADP and inorganic phosphate are quickly converted back into ATP. The total energy stored in all the ATP molecules of a cell can supply the energy requirements of that cell for less than one minute.

CELLULAR RESPIRATION

Cellular respiration is the utilization of oxygen by cells for the production of ATP. It is a series of over 20 reactions that can be divided into four phases:

(1) Glycolysis : the breakdown of 1 glucose molecule to form 2 molecules of pyruvic acid. There is a net production of 2 molecules of ATP by *substrate phosphorylation.*

(2) Formation of Acetyl Coenzyme A : the conversion of pyruvic acid into acetyl coenzyme A.

(3) Krebs Cycle (Citric Acid Cycle) : the stepwise breakdown of citric acid into oxaloacetic acid. Two molecules of ATP are produced by *substrate phosphorylation.*

(4) Electron Transport Chain : the passing of electrons along a chain of carrier molecules to an oxygen molecule; there is a stepwise release of energy for the production of ATP. Oxygen must be present to accept the electrons at the end of the chain and combine with hydrogen ions to form water. This mechanism for producing ATP is called *oxidative phosphorylation.* Most of the ATP produced by cells is produced by oxidative phosphorylation (34 of the 38 ATPs produced by the oxidation of 1 glucose molecule), so it is extremely important that the respiratory system supply body cells with sufficient oxygen.

CELLULAR RESPIRATION
Overview

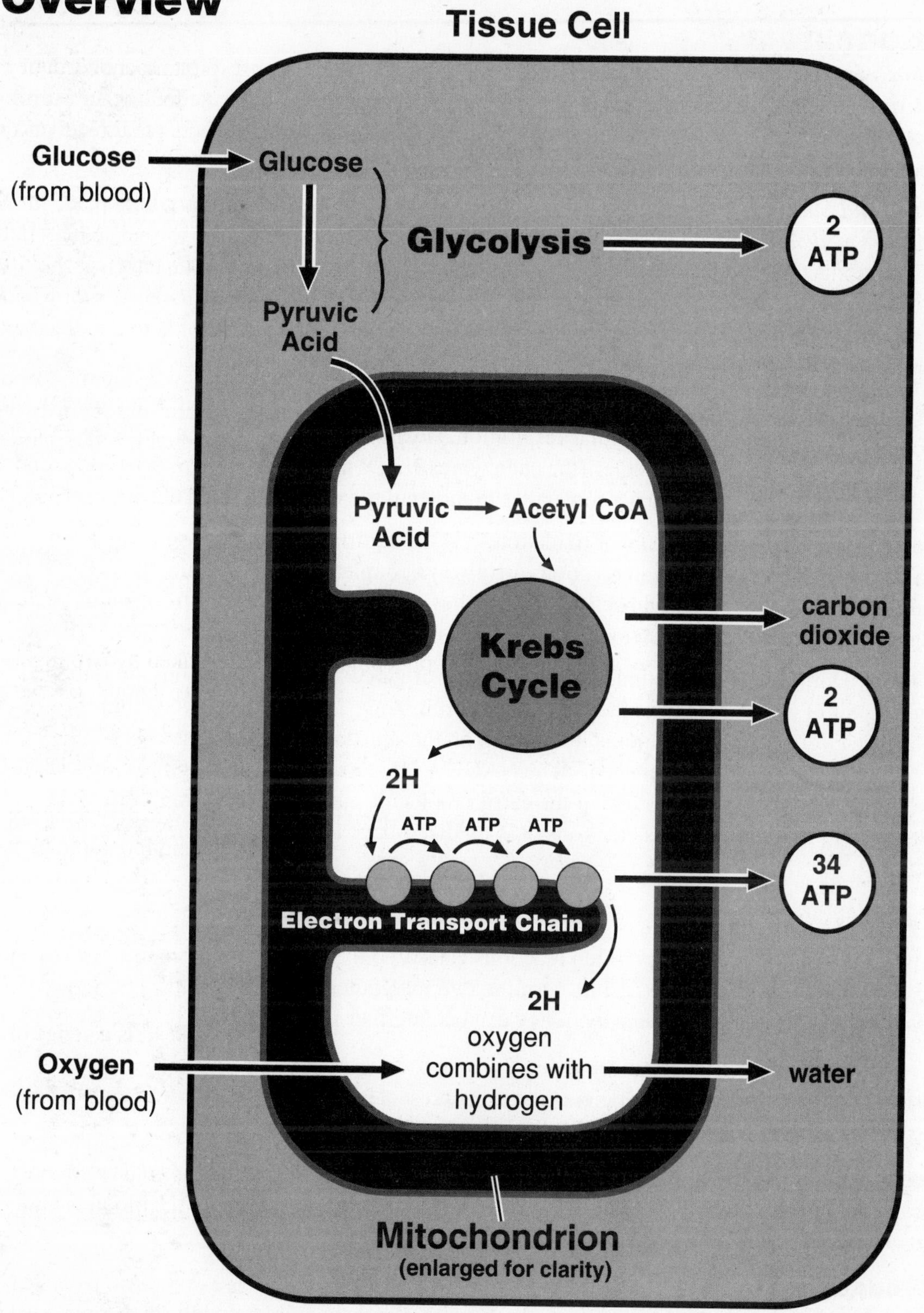

Tissue Cell

Glucose
(from blood) → **Glucose**

Glycolysis → (2 ATP)

Pyruvic Acid

Pyruvic Acid → **Acetyl CoA**

carbon dioxide

Krebs Cycle

(2 ATP)

2H

ATP ATP ATP

Electron Transport Chain

(34 ATP)

2H

oxygen combines with hydrogen → water

Oxygen
(from blood)

Mitochondrion
(enlarged for clarity)

Glucose + Oxygen + 2 ATP → Carbon Dioxide + Water + 38 ATP

CELLULAR RESPIRATION / Glycolysis

TERMINOLOGY

Oxidation-Reduction Reactions The series of reactions known as cellular respiration are oxidation-reduction reactions. This means that electrons are transferred from one molecule to another during each reaction. The molecule that loses electrons is said to be *oxidized*; the molecule that receives the same electrons is *reduced*.

Metabolites and Substrates Any molecule that is part of a sequence of reactions taking place in a cell is called a *metabolite*. In a metabolic pathway that involves many reactions, the substances that are not final products are called *intermediate metabolites*. If a reaction involves an enzyme, the metabolite may also be called a *substrate*. In glycolysis (a series of ten enzymatic reactions), when a high-energy phosphate group is transferred directly from an intermediate metabolite to a molecule of ADP (forming ATP), the process is called *substrate phosphorylation*.

Oxidation Oxidation is the removal of electrons from a molecule. This results in a decrease in the energy content of the molecule. In cellular respiration, electrons are removed in a stepwise process from glucose, carried by large molecules (the coenzymes NAD^+ and FAD) into mitochondria, and passed along a chain of electron carrier molecules to molecular oxygen (the final electron acceptor).

Reduction Reduction is the opposite of oxidation; it is the addition of electrons to a molecule. Within a cell oxidation and reduction reactions are always coupled. One molecule loses electrons and another molecule gains them. In cellular respiration, the electrons removed from a glucose molecule are accepted by an oxygen molecule (which is therefore reduced).

$NADH + H^+$ During several reactions in the oxidation of glucose, 2 hydrogen ions are removed along with a pair of electrons; this is the equivalent of removing 2 neutral hydrogen atoms (2 H). When NAD^+ picks up 2 hydrogen atoms it is shown on the illustration to the right as $NADH + H^+$. In this reaction, NAD^+ has been reduced. The $NADH + H^+$ carries its electrons into a mitochondrion, where they are transferred to one of the carrier molecules in the electron transport chain. When the $NADH + H^+$ gives up its electrons, it is oxidized back to NAD^+, and the carrier molecule is reduced.

GLYCOLYSIS

The term glycoysis refers to a series of ten reactions catalyzed by enzymes that occur in the cytosol of a cell. One molecule of glucose is split, forming two molecules of pyruvic acid. The series of reactions is called the *glycolytic pathway*. They can occur either in the presence or absence of oxygen.

Aerobic Glycolysis When sufficient oxygen is present, the glycolytic pathway ends with pyruvic acid.

Anaerobic Glycolysis In the absence of sufficient oxygen, pyruvic acid is converted into lactic acid. This occurs during vigorous exercise when the supply of oxygen by the blood cannot keep up with the needs of ATP production.

ATP Production

Substrate Phosphorylation (2 ATP) During both aerobic and anaerobic glycolysis there is a net production of 2 molecules of ATP per molecule of glucose by substrate phosphorylation.

Oxidative Phosphorylation (6 ATP) During aerobic glycolysis 2 molecules of $NADH + H^+$ are carried from reaction 6 of the glycolytic pathway into a mitochondrion. Each molecule of NADH produces 3 molecules of ATP by oxidative phosphorylation in the electron transport chain.

50

GLYCOLYSIS
The Oxidation of Glucose to Pyruvic Acid

Energy Yield for 1 Molecule of Glucose : 8 ATP

2 ATP (net production) by Substrate Phosphorylation
2 NADH (produces 6 ATP in the Electron Transport Chain)

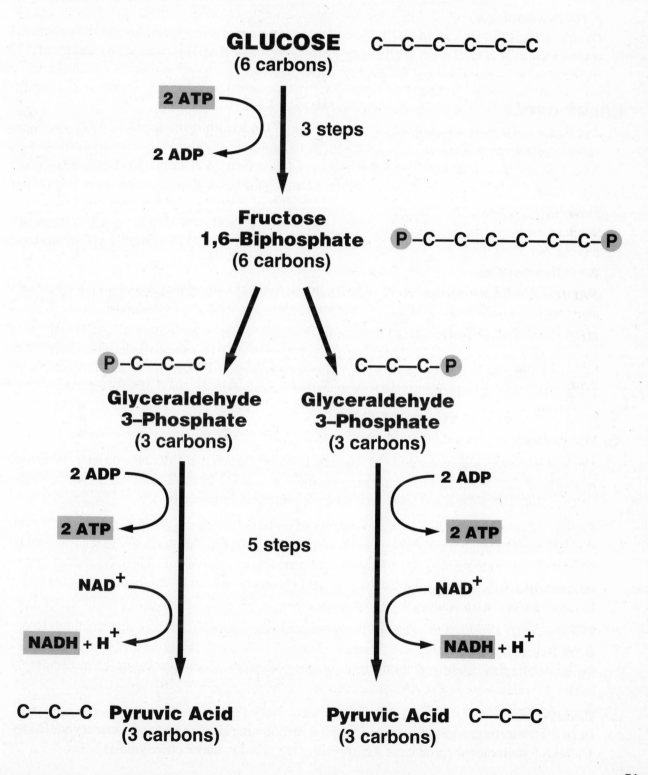

GLUCOSE C—C—C—C—C—C
(6 carbons)

2 ATP

2 ADP

3 steps

Fructose 1,6–Biphosphate P—C—C—C—C—C—C—P
(6 carbons)

P–C—C—C

Glyceraldehyde 3–Phosphate
(3 carbons)

C—C—C–P

Glyceraldehyde 3–Phosphate
(3 carbons)

2 ADP

2 ATP

2 ADP

2 ATP

5 steps

NAD^+

$NADH + H^+$

NAD^+

$NADH + H^+$

C—C—C **Pyruvic Acid**
(3 carbons)

Pyruvic Acid C—C—C
(3 carbons)

CELLULAR RESPIRATION / Krebs Cycle

FORMATION OF ACETYL COENZYME A

When oxygen is plentiful, the 2 molecules of pyruvic acid produced by glycolysis enter a mitochondrion and are converted into 2 molecules of acetyl coenzyme A (acetyl CoA). Acetyl coenzyme A links glycolysis, which occurs in the cytosol, with the Krebs cycle, which occurs in the matrix of mitochondria.

ATP Production

Oxidative Phosphorylation (6 ATP) During the conversion of pyruvic acid to acetyl coenzyme A, two molecules of NADH + H⁺ are formed. Each molecule of NADH produces 3 molecules of ATP by oxidative phosphorylation in the electron transport chain.

KREBS CYCLE

The Krebs cycle is also called the citric acid cycle or the tricarboxylic acid (TCA) cycle. It is a series of reactions that occur in the matrix of mitochondria. In this cycle, a series of oxidation-reduction reactions transfers the chemical energy in the form of electrons to coenzymes (NAD⁺ and FAD). The cycle begins when an acetyl group combines with oxaloacetic acid to form citric acid. Citric acid is broken down in a series of reactions, ending in the reformation of oxaloacetic acid. In the process, electrons are removed by coenzymes and carried to the electron transport chain and 4 molecules of ATP are formed per molecule of glucose by substrate phosphorylation.

ATP Production

Substrate Phosphorylation (2 ATP) During the Krebs cycle, two molecules of GTP are formed by substrate phosphorylation. GTP (guanosine triphosphate) is the equivalent of ATP.

Oxidative Phosphorylation (22 ATP) During the Krebs cycle, 6 molecules of NADH + H⁺ are formed; each molecule of NADH produces 3 molecules of ATP by oxidative phosphorylation in the electron transport chain (total of 18 ATP). Also, 2 molecules of FADH₂ are formed; each molecule of FADH₂ produces 2 molecules of ATP by oxidative phosphorylation (total of 4 ATP).

Summary of Reactions (1 Cycle)

One molecule of glucose produces two acetyl fragments, and, therefore, two cycles.

Citric Acid (6-carbon molecule) In reaction 1, acetyl coenzyme A donates its acetyl fragment to oxaloacetic acid, forming the 6-carbon molecule, citric acid. In this reaction a 2-carbon fragment is combined with a 4-carbon molecule, forming a 6-carbon molecule.

Carbon Dioxide Production Two molecules of carbon dioxide are released during each cycle; they are formed when a carboxyl group (—COOH) is split off; this occurs in reactions 3 and 4. The carbon dioxide formed is the major waste product of metabolism. The oxygen that appears in the carbon dioxide is derived from the carboxyl groups of the Krebs cycle intermediates (not from molecular oxygen transported from the lungs).

Coenzyme-2H Production Pairs of hydrogen atoms are transferred from intermediates to coenzyme molecules at reactions 3, 4, 5, and 7. These 4 coenzyme-2H molecules (formed during each cycle) donate their hydrogen atoms to the electron transport chain, producing 11 molecules of ATP by oxidative phosphorylation.

End Products

Each 2-carbon fragment (1 cycle) produces: 2 carbon dioxide, 1 ATP, and 4 coenzyme-H.
Each glucose molecule produces: 4 carbon dioxide, 2 ATP, and 8 coenzyme-H.

KREBS CYCLE

Pyruvic Acid to Acetyl CoA

Energy Yield for 1 Molecule of Glucose : 6 ATP

2 NADH (produces 6 ATP in the Electron Transport Chain)

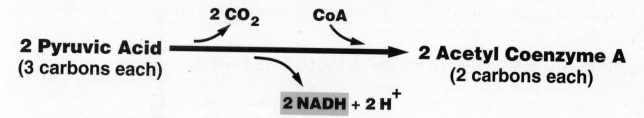

2 CO$_2$ **CoA**

2 Pyruvic Acid ⟶ **2 Acetyl Coenzyme A**
(3 carbons each)   (2 carbons each)

2 NADH + 2 H$^+$

Krebs Cycle (2 cycles per molecule of glucose)

Energy Yield for 1 Molecule of Glucose : 24 ATP

2 ATP (GTP) by Substrate Phosphorylation
6 NADH (produces 18 ATP in the Electron Transport Chain)
2 FADH$_2$ (produces 4 ATP in the Electron Transport Chain)

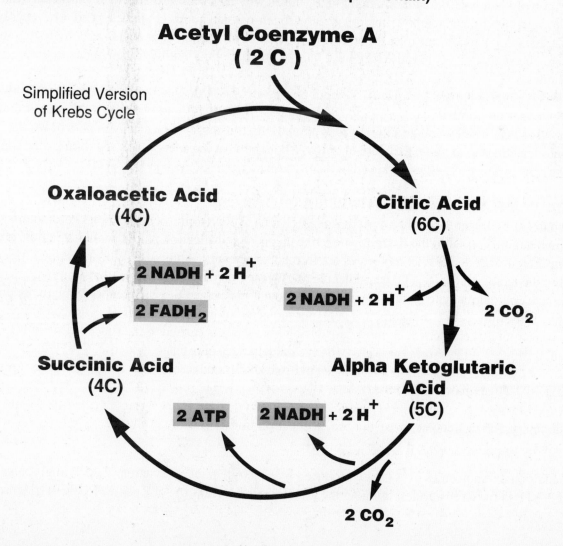

**Acetyl Coenzyme A
(2 C)**

Simplified Version
of Krebs Cycle

Oxaloacetic Acid
(4C)

Citric Acid
(6C)

2 NADH + 2 H$^+$

2 FADH$_2$

2 NADH + 2 H$^+$

2 CO$_2$

Succinic Acid
(4C)

**Alpha Ketoglutaric
Acid**
(5C)

2 ATP   2 NADH + 2 H$^+$

2 CO$_2$

CELLULAR RESPIRATION / Electron Transport Chain

The electron transport system is a chain of enzymes located on the inner membranes of the mitochondria (on the shelflike cristae). It is here where ATP is produced by oxidative phosphorylation.

Phosphorylation   Phosphorylation means adding a phosphate group to a molecule—in this case a phosphate group is added to a molecule of ADP, forming ATP.

Oxidative Phosphorylation   Oxygen must be present for this reaction to occur, so the process is called oxidative phosphorylation.

COENZYME 2–H MOLECULES (from Krebs Cycle and Glycolysis)

In each turn of the Krebs cycle, four pairs of hydrogen atoms are removed by the action of specific enzymes (dehydrogenases). Pairs of hydrogen atoms are also removed during glycolysis. These pairs of hydrogen atoms are carried to the electron transport system by coenzymes. They donate their electrons to the electron transport chain and become hydrogen ions, which diffuse into the aqueous matrix of the mitochondrion. The electrons are passed along the chain until they reach cytochrome oxidase, which transfers the electrons to oxygen, the final electron acceptor. As each atom of oxygen accepts two electrons, two hydrogen ions are taken up from the aqueous medium to form water.

ENERGY TRANSFER

Carbon-hydrogen bonds are energy-rich bonds; this is why hydrocarbons are excellent fuels. Carbon-oxygen bonds (as in carbon dioxide) and hydrogen-oxygen bonds (as in water) are low-energy bonds; breaking these bonds releases relatively little energy. Wood, natural gas, carbohydrates, and fats are all excellent fuels because they have a large number of carbon-hydrogen bonds in their molecules.

When a fuel is burned (oxidized), the high-energy carbon-hydrogen bonds are broken and low-energy bonds are formed (carbon dioxide and water are formed). There is a net loss of energy that is released as heat when wood or natural gas is burned. As the energy-rich electrons pass down the chain of enzymes to oxygen, they lose energy. About 60% of the energy released during electron transport is lost as heat; 40% is trapped in the high-energy phosphate bonds of ATP.

SUMMARY OF ATP PRODUCTION

The pairs of hydrogen atoms removed during the Krebs cycle (from isocitrate, alpha-ketoglutarate, and malate) are carried to the first enzyme in the chain. As an electron pair is passed along the chain, energy is removed and 3 ATP molecules are formed; as a result, a total of 9 ATP are formed for each turn of the Krebs cycle; 18 ATP per molecule of glucose. A pair of hydrogen atoms removed from succinate (an intermediate metabolite in the Krebs cycle) is carried to a different enzyme in the chain, Co Q. Thus, only 2 ATP are formed; 4 ATP per molecule of glucose. A pair of hydrogen atoms removed from glyceraldehyde 3-phosphate during glycolysis is carried to the first enzyme in the chain, forming 3 ATP. Since there are two glyceraldehyde 3-phosphate / glucose, 6 ATP are formed. A pair of hydrogen atoms are removed when pyruvic acid is converted to an acetyl group; as a result, another 6 ATP are produced.

In summary, for each molecule of glucose the electron transport chain produces:

$$18 + 4 + 6 + 6 = 34 \text{ ATP}$$

An additional 4 molecules of ATP are produced by substrate phosphorylation (2 ATP in glycolysis and 2 ATP in the Krebs cycle), bringing the total to 38 molecules of ATP per molecule of glucose.

ELECTRON TRANSPORT CHAIN

High-energy electrons are carried by NADH and $FADH_2$ to the electron transport chain located on the inner membrane of mitochondria. As the electrons are passed along a chain of carrier molecules, there is a stepwise release of energy for the generation of ATP.

Energy Yield for 1 Molecule of Glucose : 34 ATP

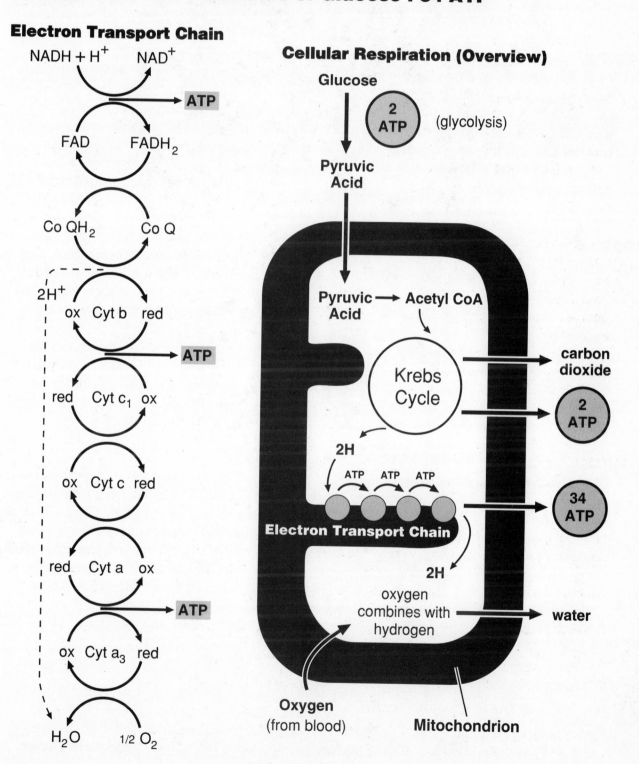

Electron Transport Chain

$NADH + H^+$ → NAD^+

ATP

FAD → $FADH_2$

$Co\ QH_2$ → Co Q

$2H^+$

ox Cyt b red

ATP

red Cyt c_1 ox

ox Cyt c red

red Cyt a ox

ATP

ox Cyt a_3 red

H_2O $1/2\ O_2$

Cellular Respiration (Overview)

Glucose

2 ATP (glycolysis)

Pyruvic Acid

Pyruvic Acid → Acetyl CoA

Krebs Cycle

carbon dioxide

2 ATP

2H

ATP ATP ATP

Electron Transport Chain

34 ATP

2H
oxygen combines with hydrogen

water

Oxygen (from blood)

Mitochondrion

Part II : Self-Testing Exercises

Unlabeled illustrations from Part I

RESPIRATORY STRUCTURES

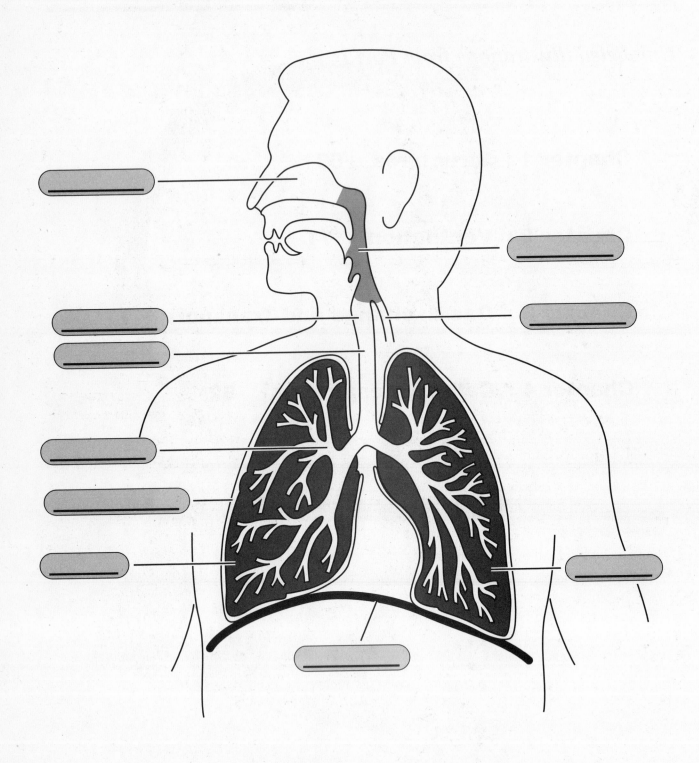

NOSE AND PHARYNX

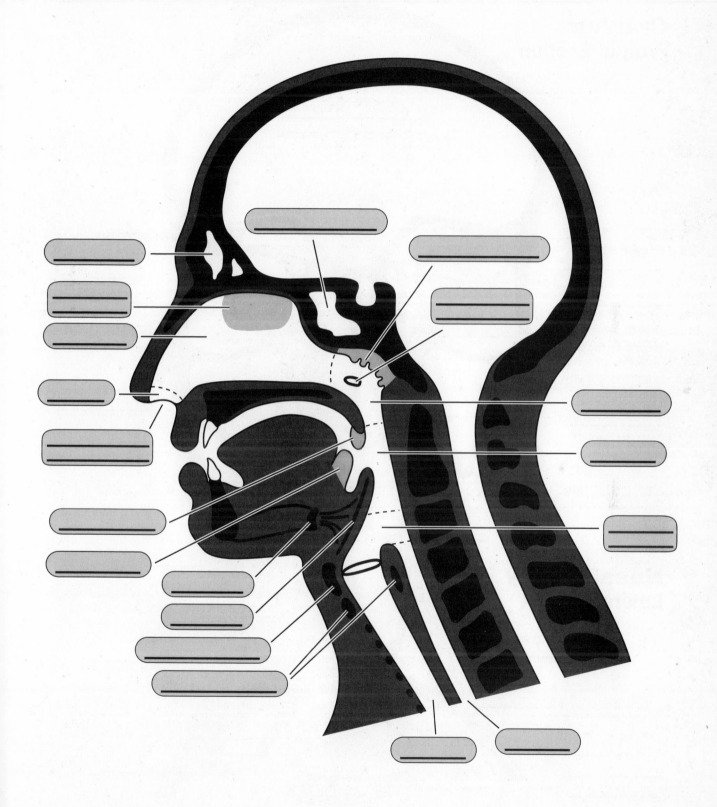

NASAL CAVITIES AND SINUSES

Cranium
Frontal Section

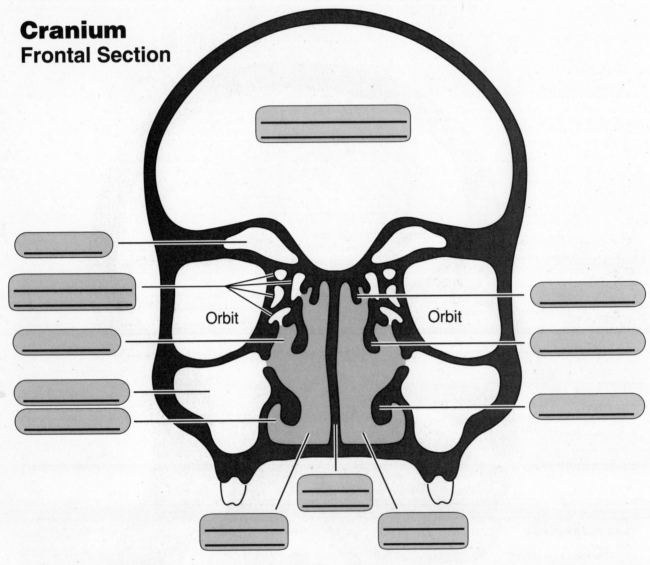

Orbit Orbit

Nasal Cavity
Lateral View

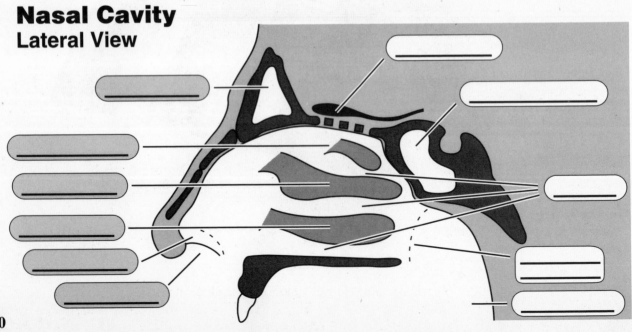

PARANASAL SINUSES

Skull
Anterior View

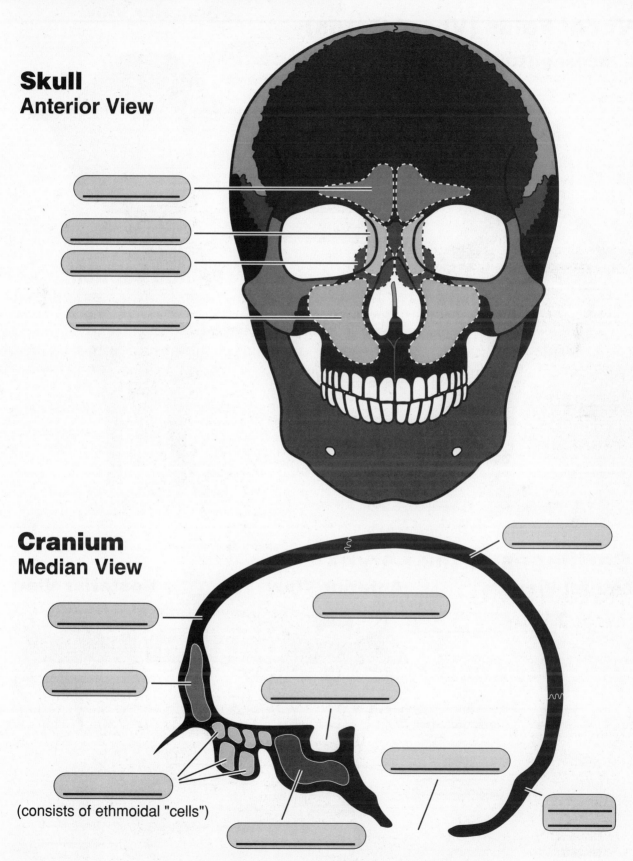

Cranium
Median View

(consists of ethmoidal "cells")

note : maxillary sinus is not visible in this illustration

LARYNX

Vocal Folds (Vocal Cords)

Midsagittal Section

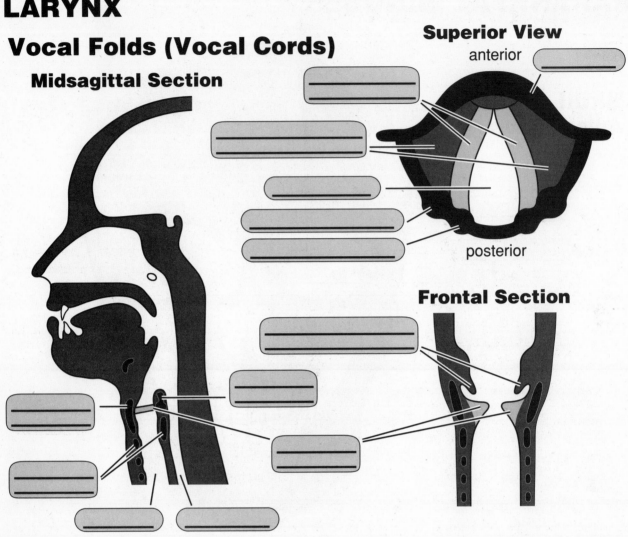

Superior View

anterior

posterior

Frontal Section

Cartilages of the Larynx

Lateral View

Anterior View

Posterior View

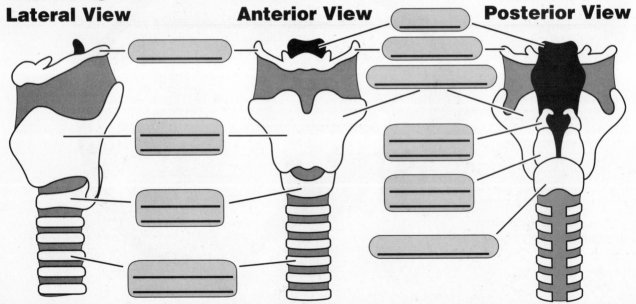

BRONCHIAL TREE

**Location
of Bronchial Tree**

**Branches
of Bronchial Tree**

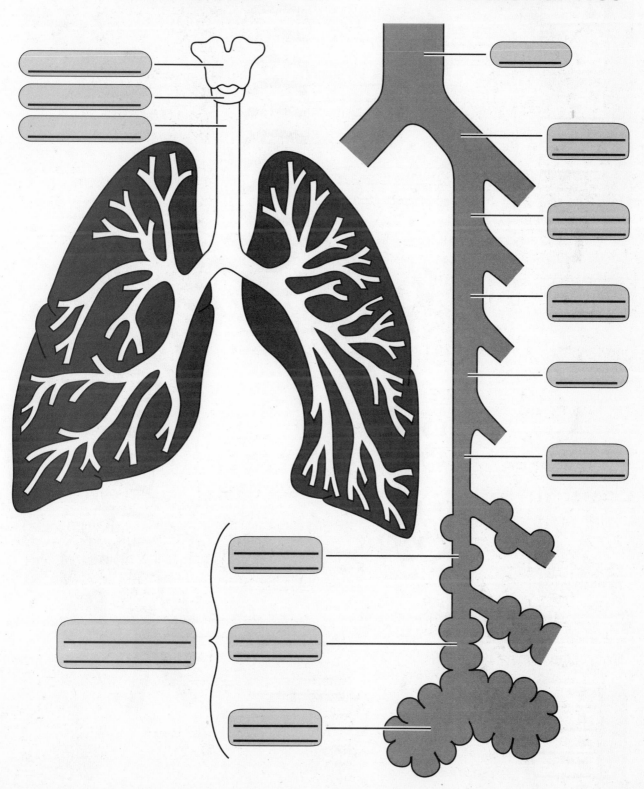

BRONCHIAL TREE : Conducting Portion

lining of the trachea and bronchi

lining of the terminal bronchioles

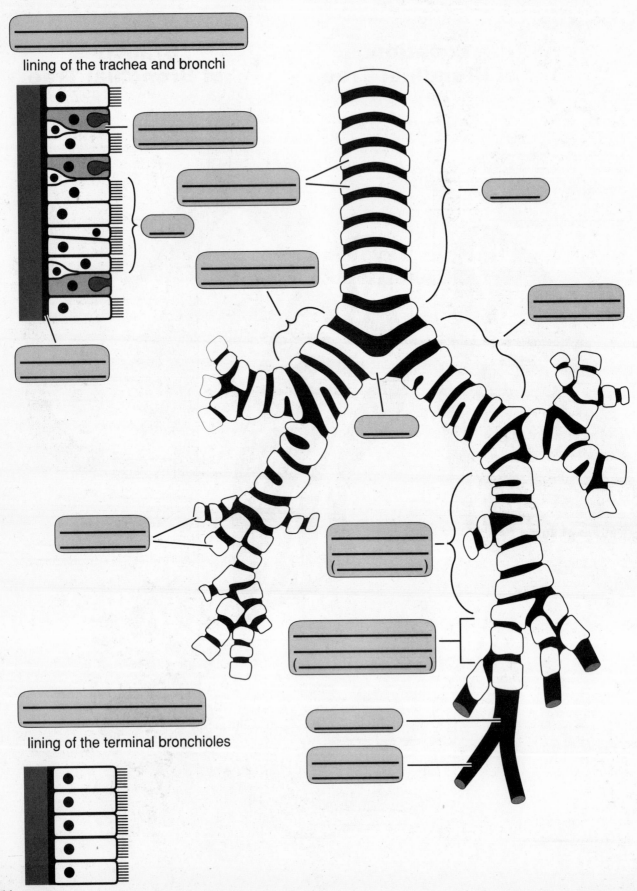

BRONCHIAL TREE : Respiratory Portion

Lobule

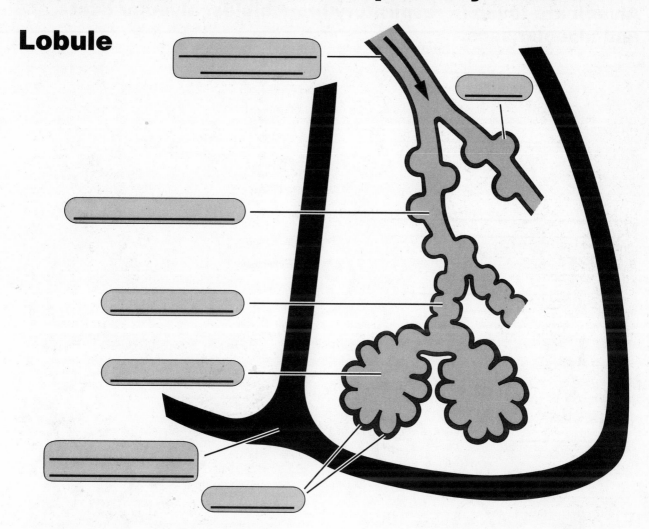

Alveolus (blood supply)

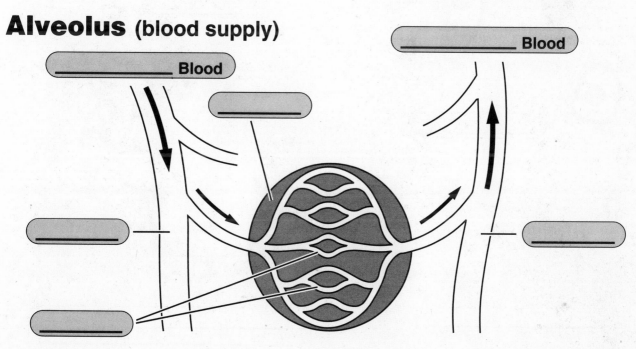

Blood

Blood

ALVEOLI
Alveoli are found in respiratory bronchioles, alveolar ducts, and alveolar sacs.

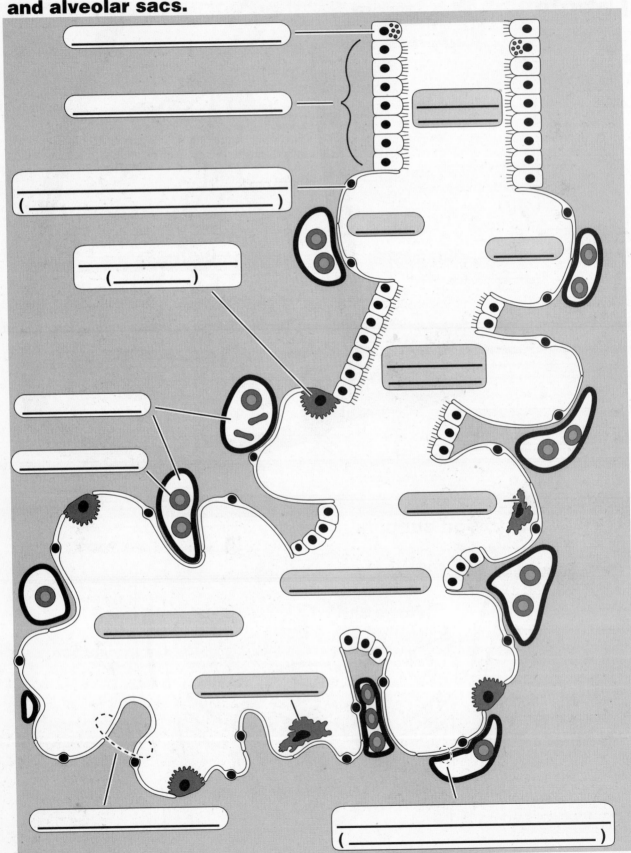

LUNGS

Location of the Lungs in the Thorax

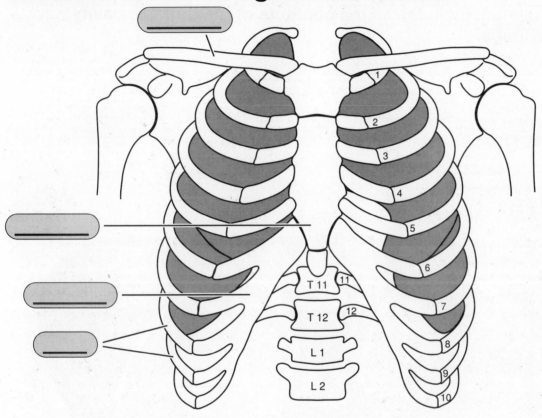

Lobes of the Lungs

Right Lung

Left Lung

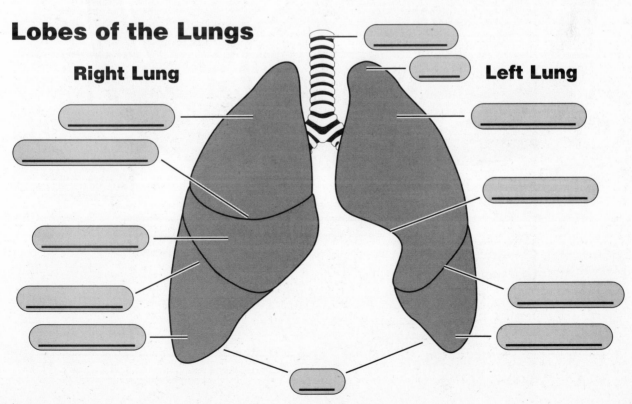

LUNGS : Transverse Section

Transverse section at the level of the 6th thoracic vertebra.

The mediastinum includes all the contents of the thoracic cavity *except* the lungs.

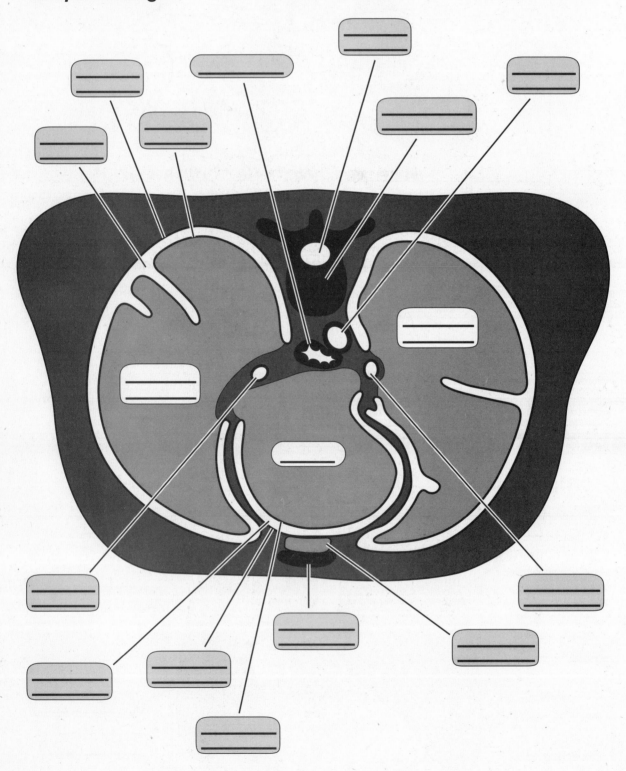

BLOOD SUPPLY TO LUNGS

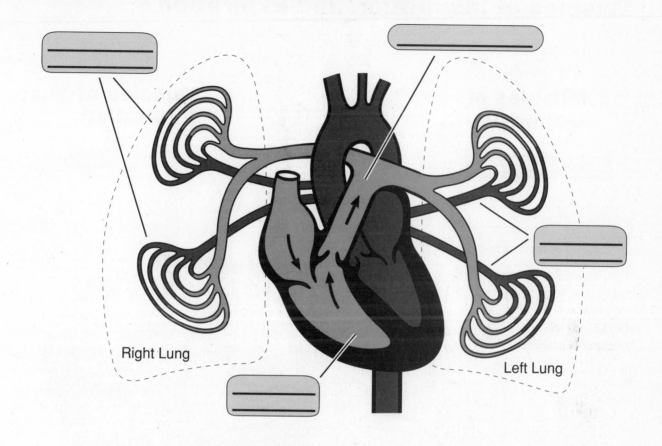

Right Lung

Left Lung

Alveoli and Capillaries

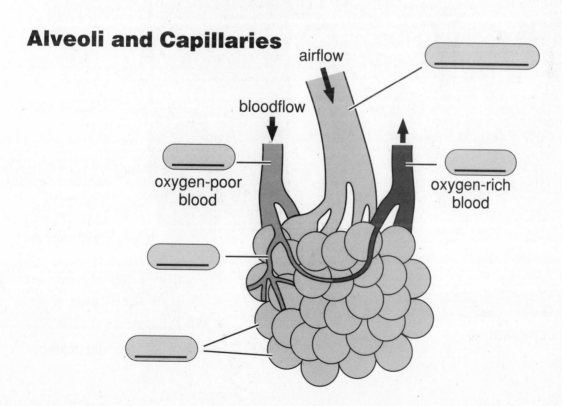

airflow

bloodflow

oxygen-poor
blood

oxygen-rich
blood

RESPIRATORY MUSCLES
Muscles of Inspiration and Expiration

Muscles of Inspiration

Muscles of Expiration

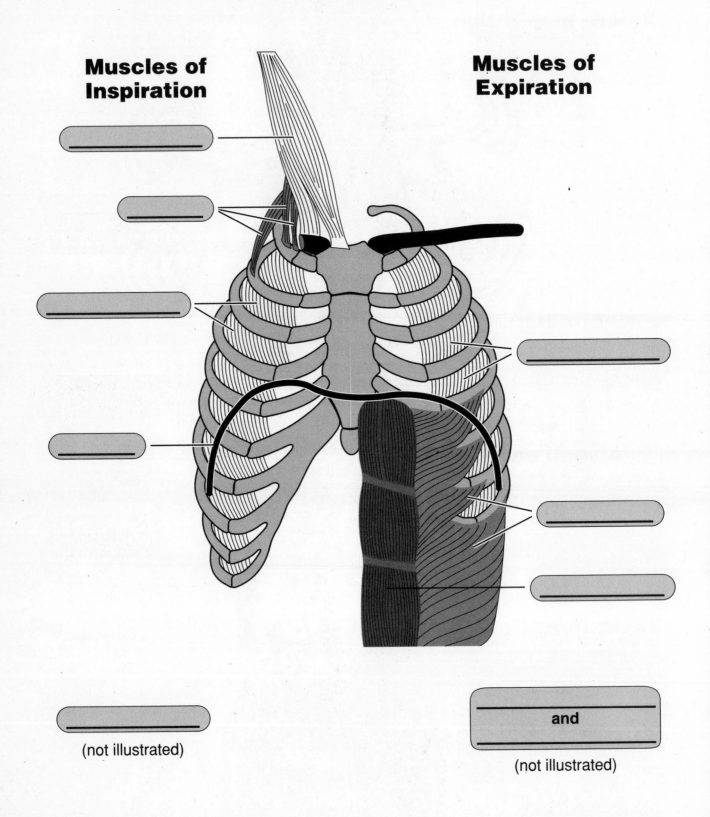

(not illustrated)

and

(not illustrated)

PRESSURE GRADIENTS

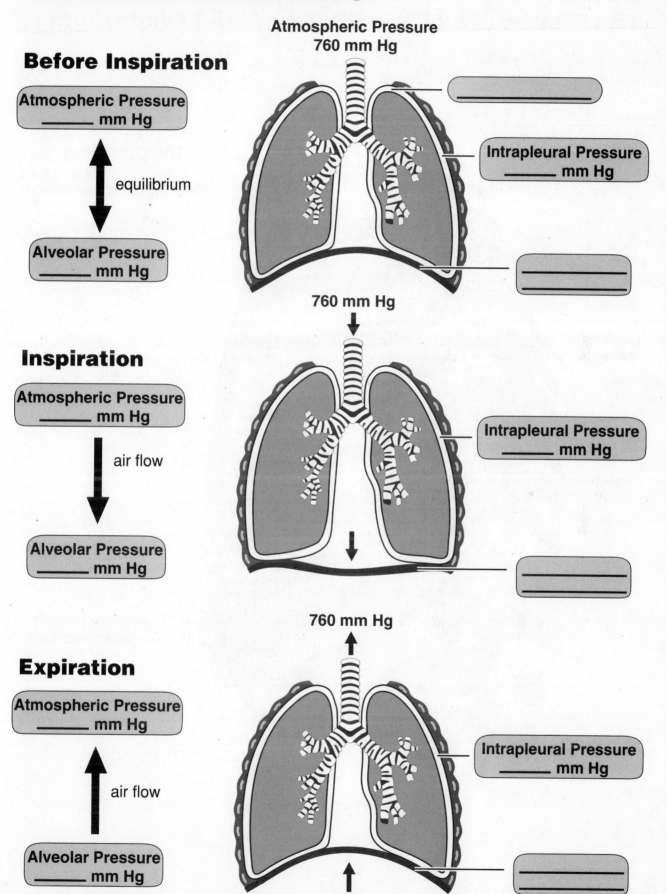

Before Inspiration

Atmospheric Pressure
760 mm Hg

Atmospheric Pressure
_____ mm Hg

equilibrium

Alveolar Pressure
_____ mm Hg

Intrapleural Pressure
_____ mm Hg

760 mm Hg

Inspiration

Atmospheric Pressure
_____ mm Hg

air flow

Alveolar Pressure
_____ mm Hg

Intrapleural Pressure
_____ mm Hg

760 mm Hg

Expiration

Atmospheric Pressure
_____ mm Hg

air flow

Alveolar Pressure
_____ mm Hg

Intrapleural Pressure
_____ mm Hg

71

LUNG VENTILATION
The Movement of the Rib Cage and Diaphragm

Increasing the space inside the _____ creates a _____ which sucks air into the lungs.

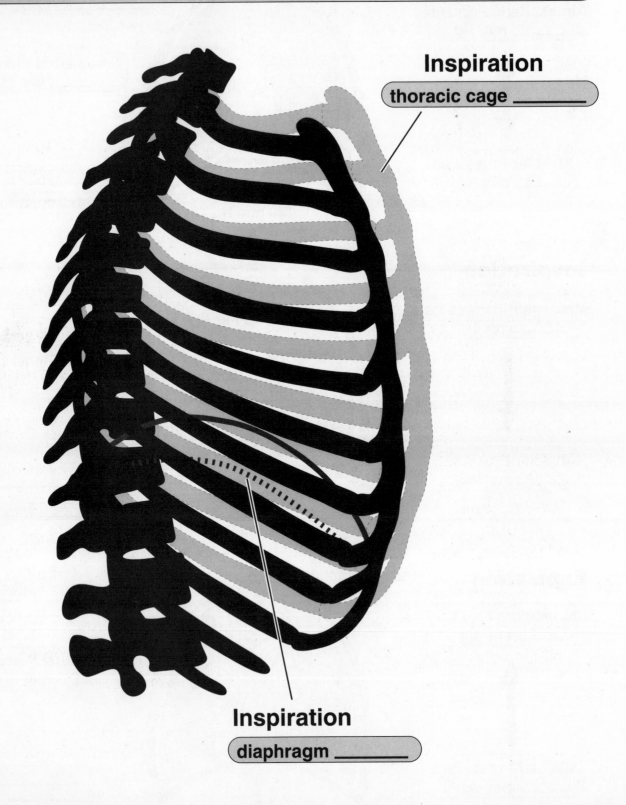

Inspiration

thoracic cage _____

Inspiration

diaphragm _____

LUNG VENTILATION
The Principal Respiratory Muscles

Inspiration :
the _____ contracts and moves _____ ;
the _____ contract, pulling the ribs upward and outward.

Expiration :
the _____ relaxes and moves _____ ;
the _____ contract (only during forced expiration).

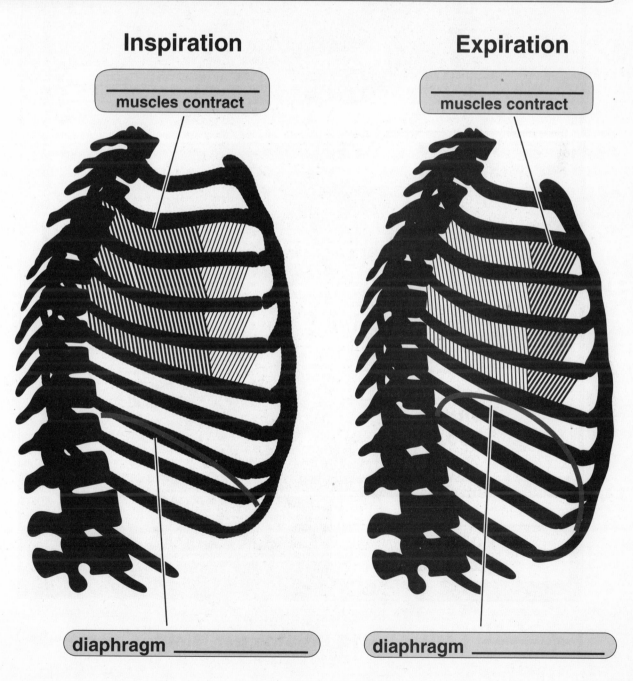

Inspiration

_____
muscles contract

diaphragm _____

Expiration

_____
muscles contract

diaphragm _____

RESPIRATORY VOLUMES

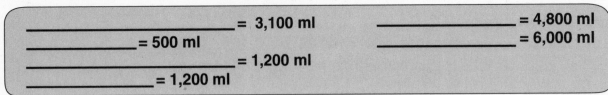

_____ = 3,100 ml   _____ = 4,800 ml
_____ = 500 ml   _____ = 6,000 ml
_____ = 1,200 ml
_____ = 1,200 ml

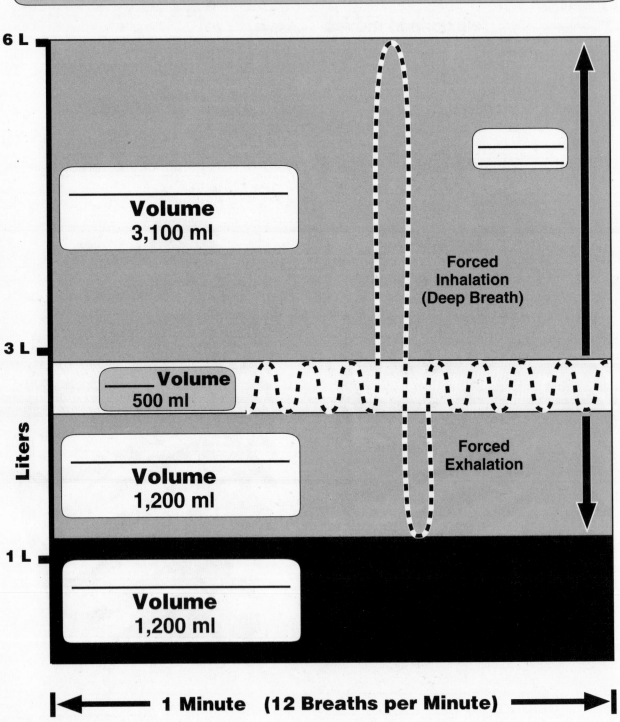

6 L

_____
**Volume
3,100 ml**

Forced
Inhalation
(Deep Breath)

3 L

_____ **Volume
500 ml**

Liters

_____
**Volume
1,200 ml**

Forced
Exhalation

1 L

_____
**Volume
1,200 ml**

|← ———————— **1 Minute   (12 Breaths per Minute)** ————————→|

ALVEOLAR VENTILATION

Dead Space

The dead space is the region of the respiratory tract where no _____ occurs.
It is approximately _____ ml of nonfunctional space.

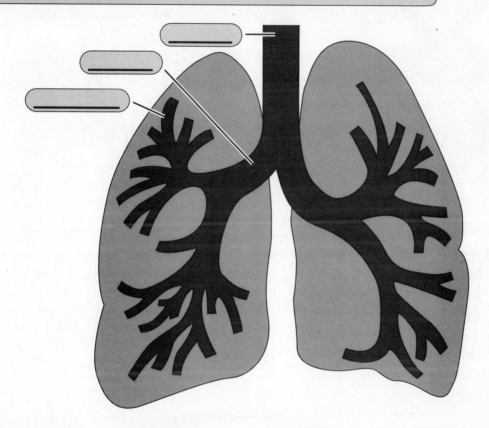

Respiratory Portion

Gas exhange occurs only in the respiratory portion, where _____ are present.
The respiratory portion includes:
respiratory _____ , _____ ducts, and alveolar sacs.

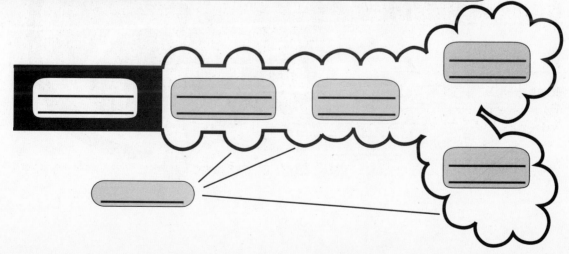

BREATHING : Nervous Control

Central Chemoreceptors
stimulated by
high carbon dioxide

(ventral view)

Carotid Bodies
stimulated by
low oxygen

Respiratory Centers
in the Brainstem

Pons { _____ center
       _____ center

Medulla { _____ area
          _____ area

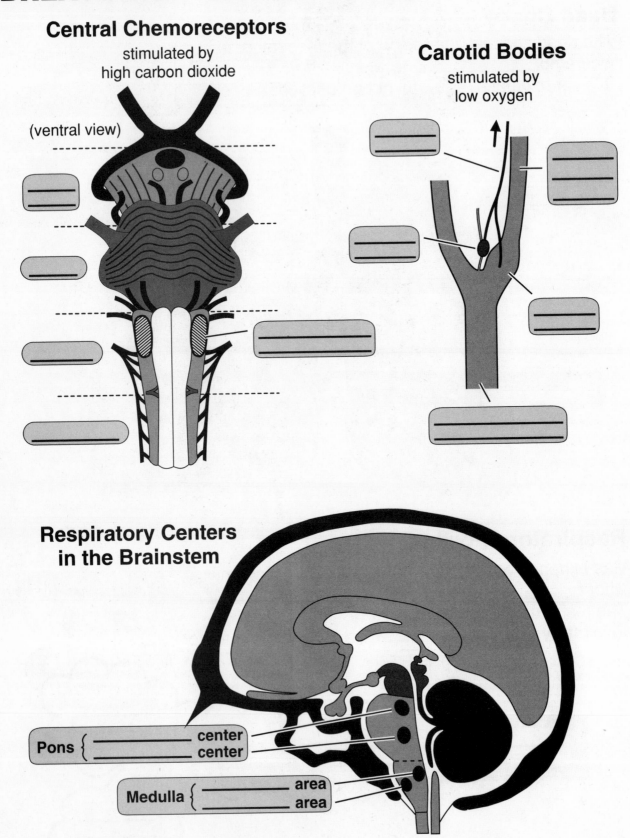

GAS EXCHANGE OVERVIEW

External (Pulmonary) Respiration

The exchange of gases between _____ and _____.

_____ Sac

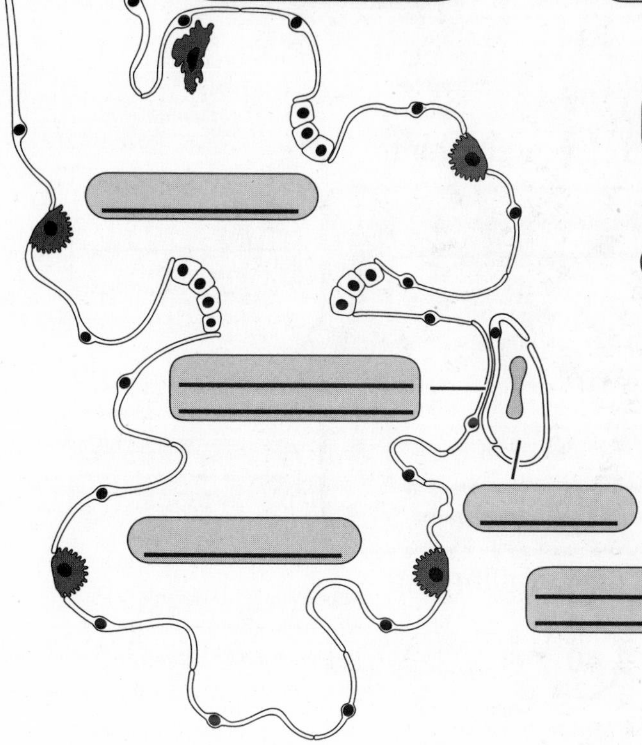

_____ Membrane

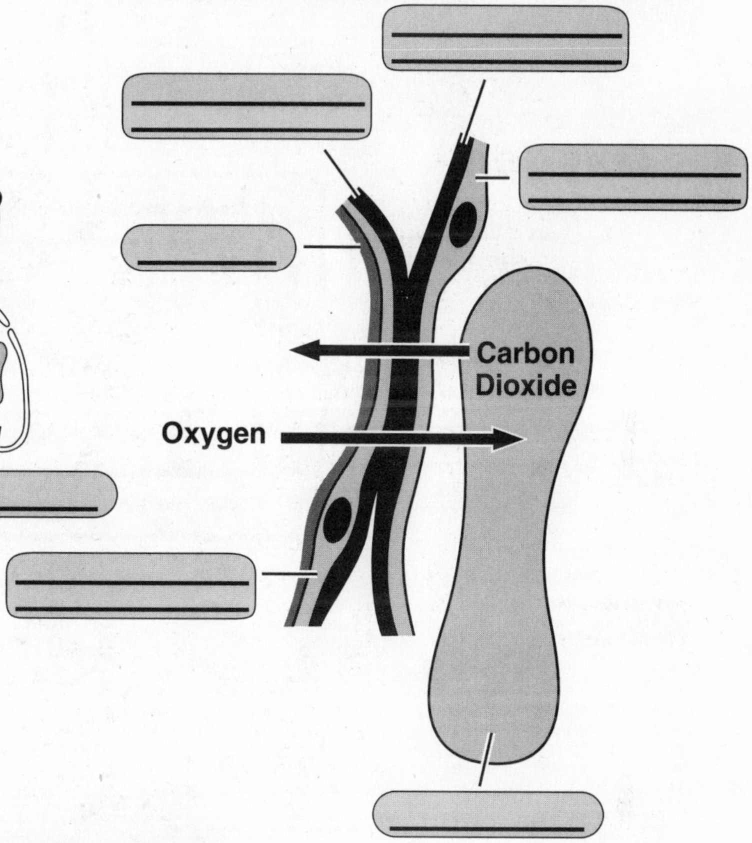

Carbon
Dioxide

Oxygen

Internal (Tissue) Respiration

The exchange of gases between _____ and _____.

$CO_2 + Hb \rightarrow$ _____

$CO_2 + H_2O \rightarrow H_2CO_3 \rightarrow H^+$

$Hb\ O_2 \rightarrow$ ___ + ___

CO_2

O_2

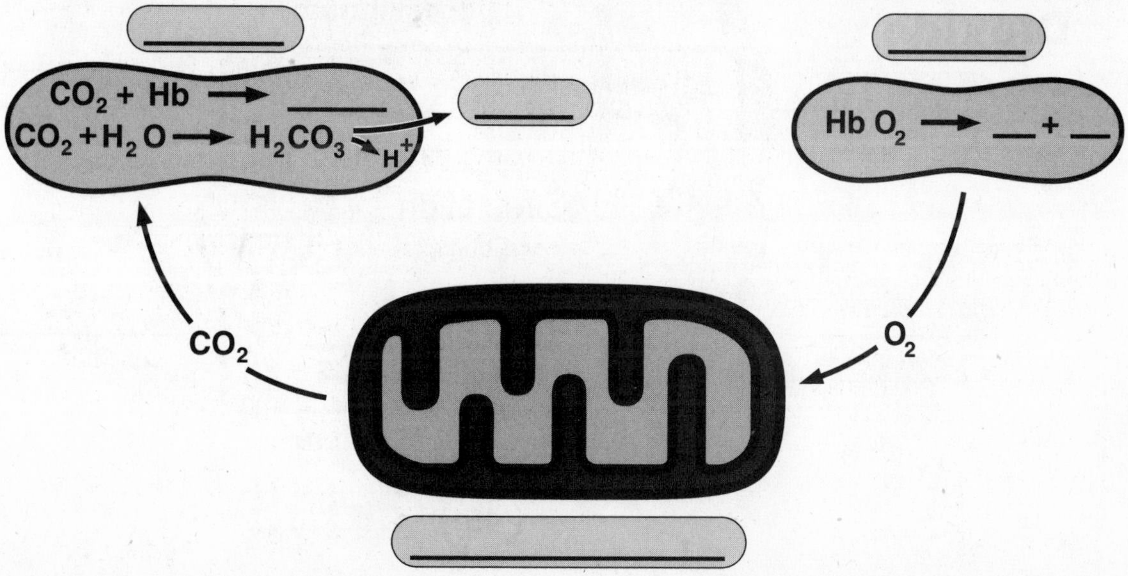

PARTIAL PRESSURES

Approximately 21% of the molecules in the air are _____ molecules.
21% of atmospheric pressure is : 0.21 x ____ mm Hg = 160 mm Hg.

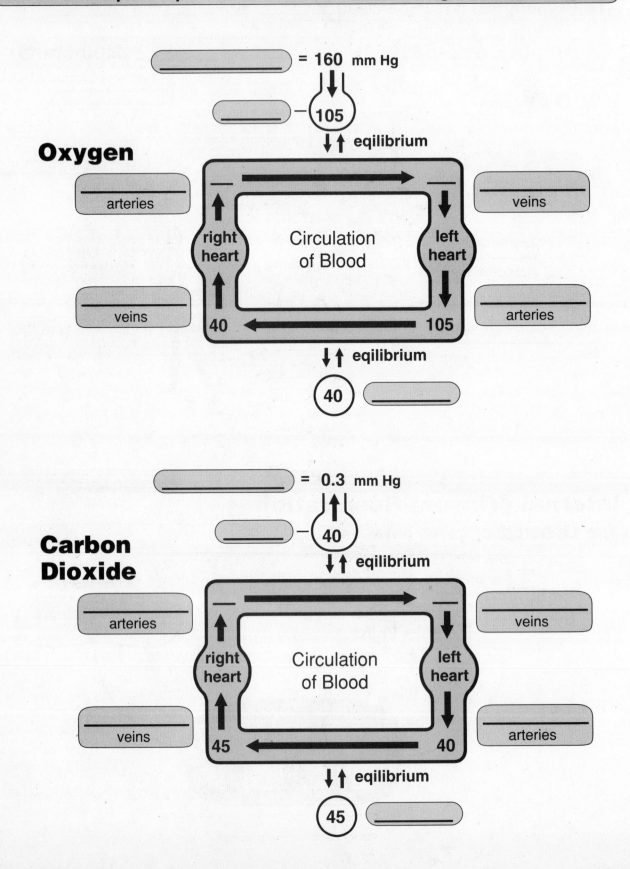

_____ = 160 mm Hg

_____ – 105

↓↑ eqilibrium

Oxygen

_____ arteries

_____ veins

right heart

Circulation of Blood

left heart

_____ veins

_____ arteries

40   105

↓↑ eqilibrium

40   _____

_____ = 0.3 mm Hg

_____ – 40

↓↑ eqilibrium

Carbon Dioxide

_____ arteries

_____ veins

right heart

Circulation of Blood

left heart

_____ veins

_____ arteries

45   40

↓↑ eqilibrium

45   _____

GAS EXCHANGE

Every minute 200 ml of _____ are absorbed by the blood plasma and 200 ml of _____ are released from the blood plasma.

Oxygen

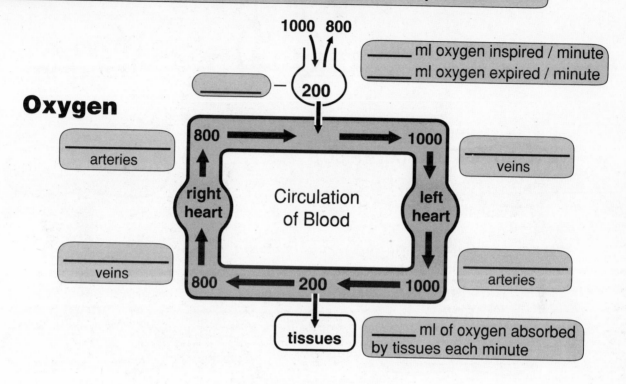

1000 800

_____ ml oxygen inspired / minute
_____ ml oxygen expired / minute

200

_____

800 _____ arteries

1000 _____ veins

right heart

Circulation of Blood

left heart

_____ veins

_____ arteries

800 200 1000

tissues

_____ ml of oxygen absorbed by tissues each minute

Carbon Dioxide

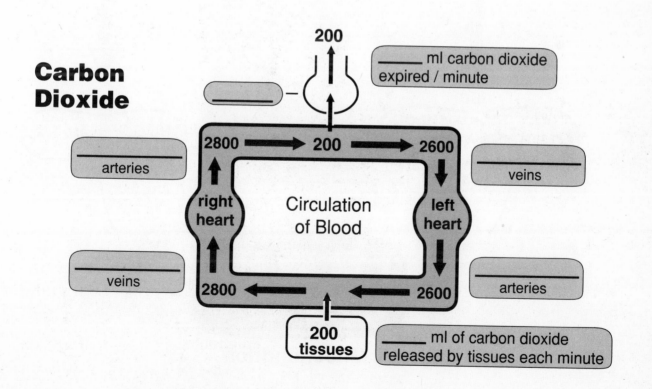

200

_____ ml carbon dioxide expired / minute

_____

2800 _____ arteries

200 2600 _____ veins

right heart

Circulation of Blood

left heart

_____ veins

_____ arteries

2800 2600

200 tissues

_____ ml of carbon dioxide released by tissues each minute

GAS TRANSPORT

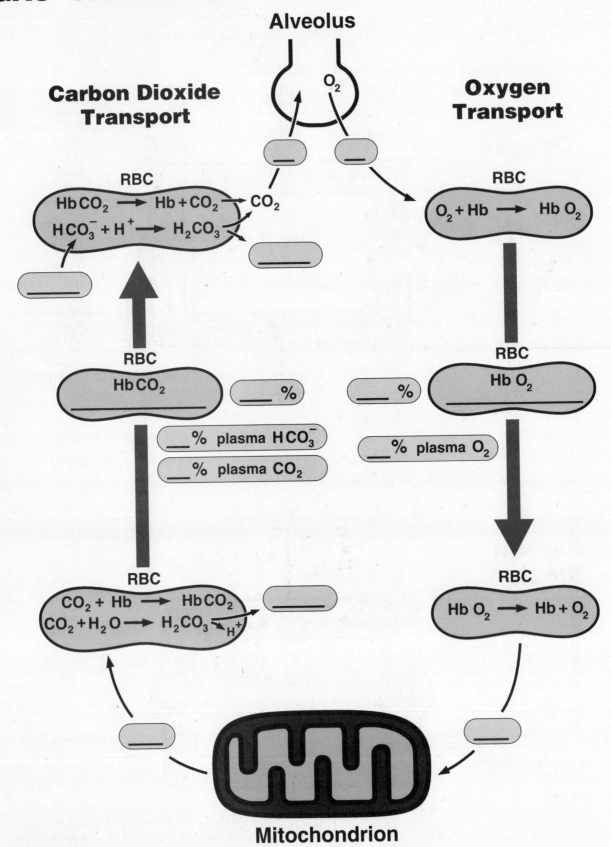

Alveolus

Carbon Dioxide Transport

Oxygen Transport

O₂

RBC

HbCO₂ → Hb + CO₂ → CO₂

HCO₃⁻ + H⁺ → H₂CO₃

RBC

O₂ + Hb → HbO₂

RBC

HbCO₂

____ %

____ %

HbO₂

____ % plasma HCO₃⁻

____ % plasma O₂

____ % plasma CO₂

RBC

CO₂ + Hb → HbCO₂

CO₂ + H₂O → H₂CO₃ → H⁺

RBC

HbO₂ → Hb + O₂

Mitochondrion

HEMOGLOBIN SATURATION

As plasma oxygen increases,
Hb saturation _____ .

In venous blood,
$p\,O_2$ is ___ mm Hg and
Hb is ___ % saturated.

In arterial blood,
$p\,O_2$ is ___ mm Hg and
Hb is ___ % saturated.

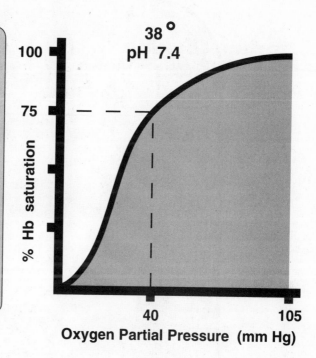

Effect of pH

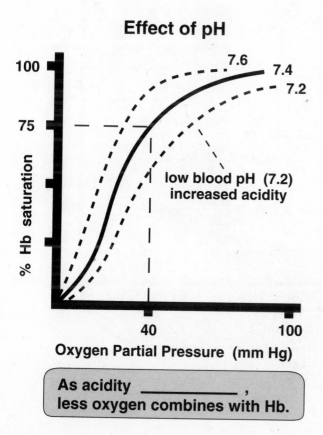

low blood pH (7.2)
increased acidity

As acidity _____ ,
less oxygen combines with Hb.

Effect of Temperature

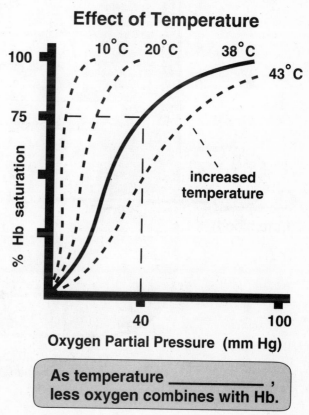

increased
temperature

As temperature _____ ,
less oxygen combines with Hb.

CELLULAR RESPIRATION
Overview

Tissue Cell

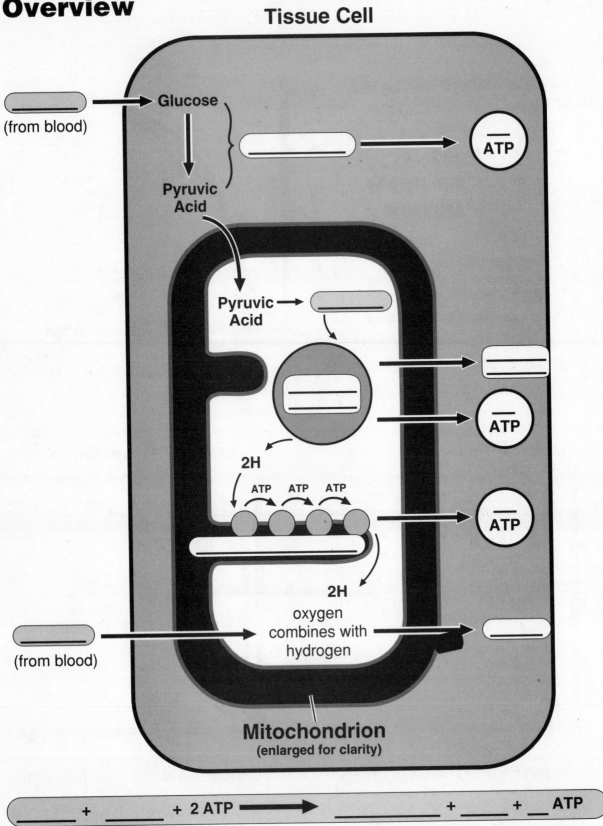

Glucose

(from blood)

$\overline{ATP}$

Pyruvic
Acid

Pyruvic
Acid

2H

ATP   ATP   ATP

$\overline{ATP}$

$\overline{ATP}$

2H
oxygen
combines with
hydrogen

(from blood)

Mitochondrion
(enlarged for clarity)

_____ + _____ + 2 ATP ➡ _____ + ____ + __ ATP

GLYCOLYSIS
The Oxidation of Glucose to Pyruvic Acid

Energy Yield for 1 Molecule of Glucose : __ ATP
2 ATP (net production) by _____ Phosphorylation
2 NADH (produces __ ATP in the Electron Transport Chain)

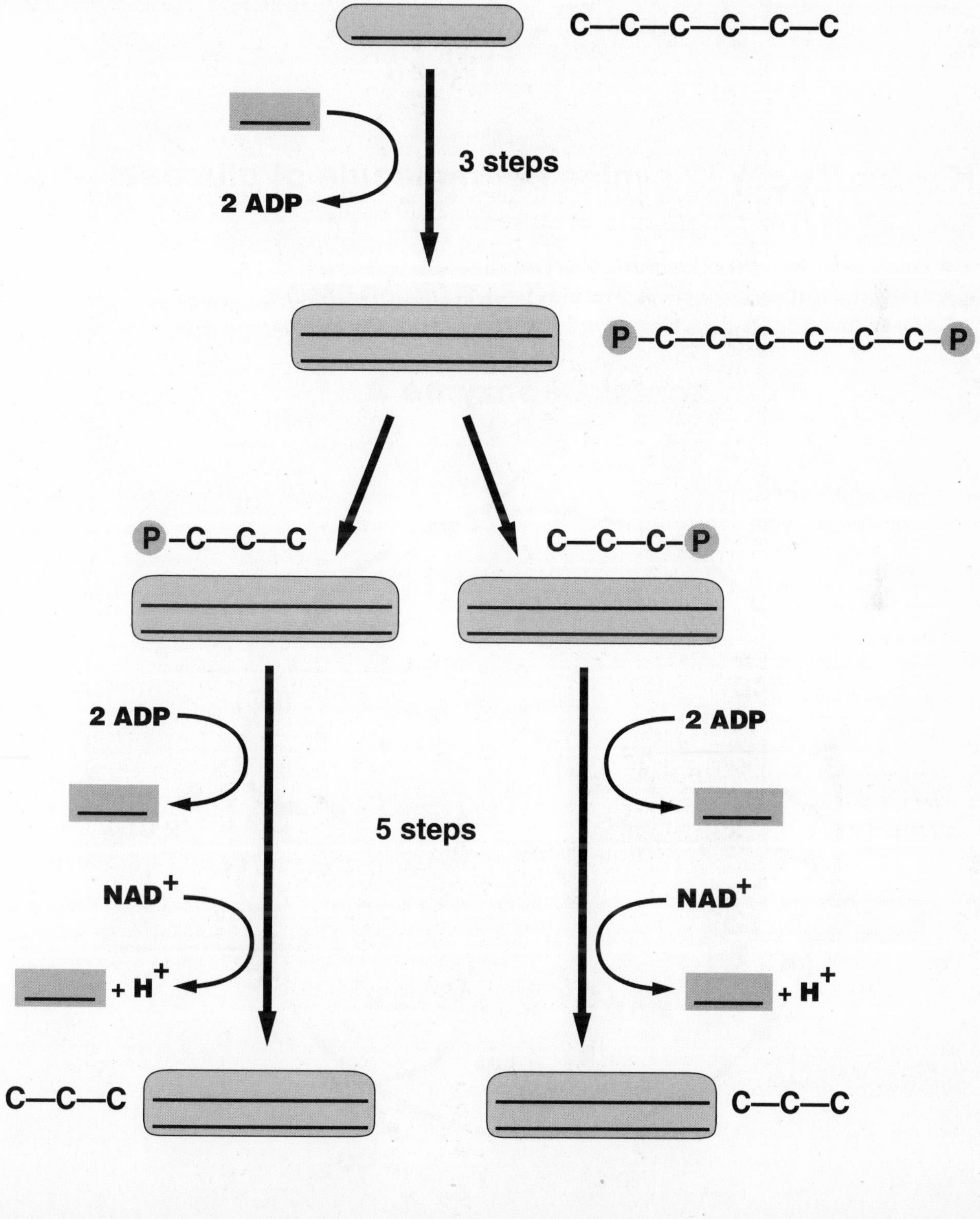

C—C—C—C—C—C

2 ADP

3 steps

P—C—C—C—C—C—P

P—C—C—C   C—C—C—P

2 ADP   2 ADP

5 steps

NAD⁺   NAD⁺

___ + H⁺   ___ + H⁺

C—C—C   C—C—C

KREBS CYCLE

Pyruvic Acid to Acetyl CoA

Energy Yield for 1 Molecule of Glucose : __ ATP

2 NADH (produces __ ATP in the Electron Transport Chain)

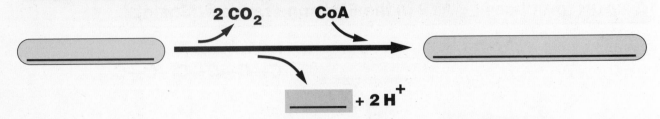

2 CO_2 CoA

_____ + 2 H$^+$

Krebs Cycle (2 cycles per molecule of glucose)

Energy Yield for 1 Molecule of Glucose : __ ATP

2 ATP (GTP) by _____ Phosphorylation
6 NADH (produces __ ATP in the Electron Transport Chain)
2 FADH$_2$ (produces __ ATP in the Electron Transport Chain)

Acetyl Coenzyme A
(2 C)

Simplified Version
of Krebs Cycle

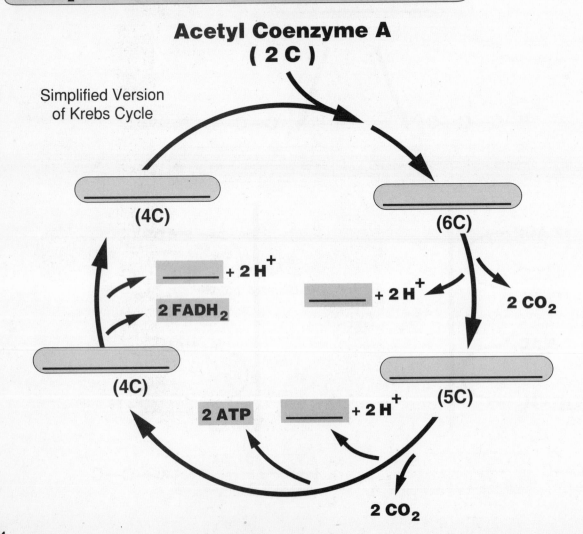

(4C)

(6C)

_____ + 2 H$^+$

2 FADH$_2$

_____ + 2 H$^+$

2 CO_2

(4C)

2 ATP   _____ + 2 H$^+$

(5C)

2 CO_2

ELECTRON TRANSPORT CHAIN

High-energy electrons are carried by _____ and _____ to the electron transport chain located on the inner membrane of _____. As the _____ are passed along a chain of _____ molecules, there is a stepwise release of energy for the generation of _____.

Energy Yield for 1 Molecule of Glucose : ___ ATP

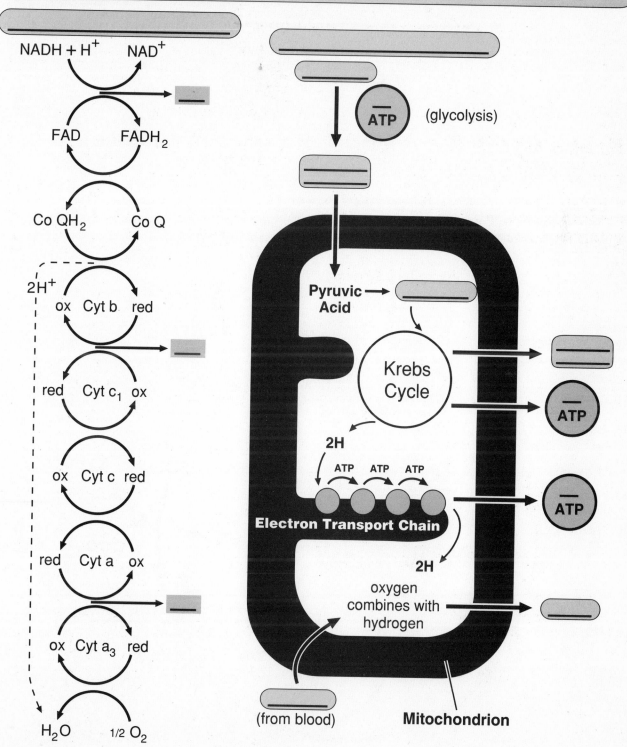

Part III : Terminology

Pronunciation Guide

Pronunciation Key

Accented Syllables

The strongest accented syllable is in capital letters : **dī - ag - NŌ - sis**

Secondary accents are indicated by a prime (′) : **fiz′ - ē - OL - ō - jē**

Vowels

Long vowels are indicated by a horizontal line (macron) above the letter :

ā as in make **ē** as in be **ī** as in ivy **ō** as in pole

Short vowels are unmarked :

e as in pet **i** as in pit **o** as in pot **u** as in bud

Other Phonetic Symbols

a as in about **oo** as in do **yoo** as in cute **oy** as in noise

acetyl CoA **AS - e - til kō - Ā**
acetyl coenzyme A **AS - e - til kō - EN - zīm Ā**
abdominal **ab - DOM - i - nal**
adenoid **AD - e - noyd**
aerobic **air - Ō - bik**
alveolar **al - VĒ - ō - lar**
alveoli **al - VĒ - ō - lī**
alveolus **al - VĒ - ō - lus**
anaerobic **an - air - Ō - bik**
aortic **ā - OR - tik**
apex **Ā - peks**
apnea **AP - nē - a**
apneustic **ap - NOO - stik**
arteriole **ar - TĒ - rē - ōl**
arytenoid **ar′- i - TĒ - noyd**
atelectasis **at′- ē - LEK - ta - sis**

biphosphoglycerate **bī - fos′- fō - GLIS - er - āt**
Bohr **BŌR**
bronchi **BRONG - kē**
bronchial **BRONG - kē - al**
bronchiole **BRONG - kē - ōl**
bronchus **BRONG - kus**

carbaminohemoglobin **kar-ba-mē-nō-HĒ-mō-glō-bin**
carbonic anhydrase **kar - BON - ik an-HĪ-drās**
carotid **ka - ROT - id**
chemoreceptor **kē′- mō - rē - SEP - tor**
chemosensitive **kē′- mō - SEN - si - tiv**
choana **KŌ - ā - na**
choanae **kō - Ā - nē**
cilia **SIL - ē - a**
ciliated **SIL - ē - āt′- ed**
cilium **SIL - ē - um**
coenzyme **kō - EN - zīm**
columnar **kol - LUM - nar**
compliance **kom - PLĪ - ans**
concha **KONG - ka**
conchae **KONG - kē**
corniculate **kor - NIK - yoo - lāt**
costal **KOS - tal**
cricoid **KRĪ - koyd**
cuneiform **kyoo - NĒ - i - form**
cytochrome **SĪ - tō - krōm**

diaphragm **DĪ - a - fram**
dorsum nasi **DOR - sum NĀ - sē**

endoderm **En - dō - derm**
epiglottis **ep′- i - GLOT - is**
epithelial **ep′- i - THĒ - lē - al**
epithelium **ep′- i - THĒ - lē - um**
esophagus **e - SOF - a - gus**
eupnea **yoop - NĒ - a**
exhalation **eks′- ha - LĀ - shun**
expiration **ek - spi - RĀ - shun**
expiratory **eks - PĪ - ra - tō′- rē**

fauces **FAW - sēz**
fissure **FISH - ur**

glottis **GLOT - is**
glyceraldehyde **glis′- er - AL - de - hīd**
glycolysis **glī - KOL - i - sis**

Haldane **HAWL - dān**

hemoglobin HĒ - mō - glō - bin
hilum HĪ - lum
hilus HĪ - lus
hypercapnia hī´- per - KAP - nē - a
hypopharynx hī´- pō - FAR - inks
hypoxia hī - POK - sē - a

inhalation in - ha - LĀ - shun
inspiration in - spi - RĀ - shun
inspiratory in - SPĪ - ra - tor - ē
intercostal in´- ter - KOS - tal
intrapleural in - tra - PLOOR - al

lactic LAK - tik
laryngeal la - RIN - jē - al
laryngopharynx la - ring´- gō - FAR - inks
laryngotracheal la - ring´- gō - TRĀ - kē - al
larynx LAR - inks
lobar LŌ - ber
lobule LOB - yool

macrophage MAK - rō - fāj
meatus mē - Ā - tus
mediastinum mē´- dē - as - TĪ - num
medullary MED - yoo - lar´- ē
mesenchymal MEZ - en - kīm - al
metabolite me - TAB - ō - līt

nares NĀ - rēz
naris NĀ - ris
nasal NĀ - zal
nasopharynx nā´- zō - FAR - inks

oblique ō - BLĒK
olfactory ol - FAK - tō - rē
oropharynx or´- ō - FAR - inks
otorhinolaryngology ō´- tō - rī - nō - lar´- in - GOL - ō - jē
oxaloacetic ok´- sa - lō - a - SĒ - tik
oxidation ok´- si - DĀ - shun
oxyhemoglobin ok´- sē - HĒ - mō - glō´- bin

palatine PAL - a - tīn
paranasal par´- a - NĀ - zal
parietal pa - RĪ - e - tal
pharyngeal fa - RIN - jē - al
pharynx FAR - inks
phosphorylation fos´- for - i - LĀ - shun
pleura PLOOR - a
pleural PLOO - ral
pneumotaxic noo´- mō - TAK - sik
proprioceptor prō´- prē - ō - SEP - tor
pseudostratified soo´- dō - STRAT - i - fīd
pulmonary PUL - mo - ner´- ē
pyruvic pī - ROO - vik

residual ri - ZID - yoo - al
respiratory rē - SPĪ - ra - tor - ē
rhythmicity rith - MIS - i - tē
rima glottidis RĪ - ma GLOT - ti - dis
rima vestibuli RĪ - ma ves - TIB - yoo - lē

scalene SKĀ - lēn
septal SEP - tal
septum SEP - tum
sinus SĪ - nus
squamous SKWĀ - mus
sternum STER - num
substrate SUB - strāt
succinate SUK - si - nāt
surfactant sur - FAK - tant

tertiary TER - shē - er - ē
thoracic thō - RAS - ik
trachea TRĀ - kē - a
trachealis trā´- kē - A - lis
turbinate TUR - bi - nāt

ventricular ven - TRIK - yoo - lar
vestibule VES - ti - byool
vibrissae vī - BRIS - ē
visceral VIS - er - al

Glossary of Terms

Abdomen   The region between the diaphragm and the pelvis.

Abdominal cavity   Superior portion of the abdominopelvic cavity. Contains the stomach, spleen, liver, gallbladder, pancreas, small intestine, and most of the large intestine.

Abdominal thrust maneuver   A first-aid procedure for choking. A quick upward thrust against the diaphragm forces air out of the lungs, resulting in the ejection of any object lodged in the trachea. Also called the *Heimlich maneuver.*

Abdominopelvic cavity   Inferior component of the ventral body cavity. It is subdivided into an upper abdominal cavity and a lower pelvic cavity.

Acetyl coenzyme A (Acetyl CoA)   A coenzyme that transfers 2-carbon acetyl groups to the Krebs cycle.

Adam's apple   *See* Thyroid cartilage.

Adenoids   *See* Pharyngeal tonsil.

Adenosine diphosphate (ADP)   When a phosphate is split from ATP, the resulting molecule contains two phosphate groups and is called ADP. The energy released during this reaction is used for cell functions.

Adenosine triphosphate (ATP)   The universal energy-carrying molecule manufactured in all living cells. It consists of adenine (a nitrogenous base), ribose (a 5-carbon sugar), and three phosphate groups.

Aerobic glycolysis   A series of reactions resulting in the breakdown of one glucose molecule into two molecules of pyruvic acid; oxygen must be present.

Alveolar-capillary membrane   The membrane in the lungs through which the diffusion of respiratory gases occurs. It consists of the epithelial cells lining the alveolus, the endothelial cells lining the capillary, and the basement membrane between them. Also called the *respiratory membrane* or the *blood-air barrier.*

Alveolar duct   A branch of a respiratory bronchiole. The walls are lined by alveoli (alveoli are not separated by cuboidal epithelial cells).

Alveolar macrophage   Macrophage (phagocyte) found in the alveolar walls of the lungs. Ingests particulate matter and bacteria that reach the alveoli. Also called a *dust cell.*

Alveolar pressure   Air pressure within the lungs (in the pulmonary alveoli). Also called *intrapulmonic pressure* or *intrapleural pressure.*

Alveolar sac   The end portion of each branch of the bronchial tree; each alveolar duct leads into two or more alveolar sacs. An expanded region containing two or more alveoli.

Alveolar ventilation   The volume of fresh air entering the alveoli each minute.

Alveolus (plural: alveoli)   A saclike outpouching of the respiratory portion of the bronchial tree. Alveolar walls are the only locations where gas exchange occurs between the lungs and the blood.

Anaerobic glycolysis   In the absence of oxygen, glucose is converted into two molecules of lactic acid.

Anatomic dead space   The volume of air in the respiratory tract that does not participate in gas exchange. Air that does not reach the alveoli in the respiratory portion of the tract.

Aortic body chemoreceptor   Receptor on or near the arch of the aorta; responds to changes in blood levels of oxygen, carbon dioxide, and hydrogen ions.

Apex   The pointed end of a conical structure. The apex of a lung is also called a *cupula.*

Apnea   The temporary cessation of breathing.

Apneustic area   A portion of the respiratory center in the pons (brain stem). It sends nerve impulses to the inspiratory area in the medulla oblongata that activate and prolong inspiration; these nerve impulses also inhibit expiration.

Arytenoid cartilages   A pair of small, pyramidal cartilages of the larynx. They attach to the vocal folds and intrinsic pharyngeal muscles and can move the vocal folds.

Atmospheric pressure   The air pressure surrounding the body. About 760 mm Hg at sea level.

ATP   See Adenosine triphosphate.

Base   The broadest part of a pyramidal structure.

Basement membrane   A thin layer of extracellular material. Consists of the basal lamina secreted by epithelial cells and the reticular lamina secreted by connective tissue cells.

Bicarbonate ion HCO_3^-.

Blood–air barrier   *See* Alveolar-capillary membrane.

Bohr effect   In an acid environment, oxygen splits more readily from hemoglobin.

Boyle's law   Relationship between the pressure and volume of a gas. The pressure of a gas in a container is inversely proportional to the volume of the container.

BPG   2, 3 – biphosphoglycerate.

Brain stem   The portion of the brain immediately superior to the spinal cord. Consists of the medulla oblongata, pons, and midbrain.

Bridge (of nose)   The superior portion of the dorsum nasi (the dorsum nasi is the rounded anterior border of the nose).

Bronchial tree   The trachea, bronchi, and their branching structures up to and including the terminal bronchioles.

Bronchiole   A branch of a tertiary bronchus.

Bronchopulmonary segment   The pyramidal shaped portion of a lung supplied by a tertiary bronchus. There are 10 in the right lung and 8 in the left lung.

Bronchus (plural: bronchi)   One of the two large branches of the trachea.

Bulk flow   The movement of large numbers of ions, molecules, or particles in the same direction, as a result of osmotic or hydrostatic pressure gradients.

Carbaminohemoglobin   Compound resulting from the combination of carbon dioxide and hemoglobin.

Carbon monoxide (CO)   A gas that reacts with hemoglobin, decreasing its oxygen-carrying capacity.

Carbonic acid (H_2CO_3)   An acid formed by combining carbon dioxide and water.

Carbonic anhydrase   An enzyme that catalyzes the conversion of carbon dioxide and water into carbonic acid.

Cardiac notch   An angular notch in the anterior border of the left lung, where the heart presses against the lung.

Carotid   Pertaining to the carotid arteries (in the neck).

Carotid body chemoreceptor   A receptor on or near the

carotid sinus that responds to blood levels of oxygen, carbon dioxide, and hydrogen ions.

Carotid sinus   A dilated region of the internal carotid artery just above the bifurcation of the common carotid artery.

Cartilage   A type of connective tissue consisting of cells called chondrocytes embedded in a dense network of collagen and elastic fibers and a matrix of chondroitin sulfate.

Cascade   A sequence of reactions in which the number of products increases at one or more of the steps.

Cellular respiration   The oxidation of glucose in the cells of the body. Glucose combines with oxygen to form carbon dioxide and water; energy in the form of ATP is released during this series of reactions.

Central chemoreceptor   A receptor in the medulla (brain stem) that responds to changes in the hydrogen ion concentration of extracellular fluid in the brain.

Charles' law   The volume of a gas is directly proportional to its absolute temperature, assuming that the pressure remains constant.

Chemoreceptor   A receptor that is sensitive to changes in the concentrations of oxygen, carbon dioxide, and hydrogen ions in the blood. There are two main types: central chemoreceptors (located in the brain) and peripheral chemoreceptors (located in blood vessels outside the brain).

Chemosensitive area   Neurons within the medulla of the brain stem that are highly sensitive to hydrogen ion concentration

Chest   *See* Thorax.

Choanae (singular: choana)   *See* Internal nares.

Cilium (plural: cilia)   A hairlike projection from a cell. May be used to move the entire cell or to move substances along the surface of the cell.

Citric acid   A 6-carbon intermediate in the Krebs cycle.

Citric acid cycle   *See* Krebs cycle.

Coenzyme   A nonprotein organic molecule that generally serves as a carrier that transfers atoms or small molecular fragments from one reaction to another. An example is NAD, which transfers hydrogen atoms from the Krebs cycle to the electron transport chain.

Coenzyme A (CoA)   A coenzyme derived from pantothenic acid (a B vitamin). It transfers an acetyl group (–COCH$_3$) from the cytosol, where it has been formed from pyruvic acid, into a mitochondrion, where it enters the Krebs cycle.

Collagen   A strong, fibrous protein that is the main extracellular structural element in connective tissue.

Compliance   Stretchability. The ease with which the lungs and thoracic wall can be expanded. Also called *lung compliance*.

Concentration   The amount of material per unit volume of a solution.

Concentration gradient   The difference in concentration between two regions. Materials move down concentration gradients from regions of high to low concentration.

Concha (plural: conchae)   A scroll-like bone on the lateral wall of a nasal cavity. Also called a *turbinate*.

Conducting portion   The portion of the respiratory tract in which gas exchange with the blood does not occur. It carries air to the respiratory portions where gas exchange occurs. It extends from the top of the trachea to the beginning of the respiratory bronchioles.

Connective tissue   The most abundant of the four basic tissue types in the body. It consists of relatively few cells and a great deal of intercellular substance that binds and supports

body structures.

Corniculate cartilages   Paired, horn-shaped pieces of elastic cartilage located at the apex of each arytenoid cartilage in the larynx.

Costal cartilage   Hyaline cartilage that attaches the first ten ribs to the sternum.

Creatine phosphate   A high-energy molecule present in skeletal muscle fibers. Used to generate ATP rapidly.

Cricoid cartilage   The most inferior of the cartilages of the larynx. Shaped like a signet ring with the band facing anteriorly.

Cuneiform cartilages   Paired, wedge-shaped pieces of elastic cartilage; anterior to the corniculate cartilages in the larynx.

Cupula (of lung)   *See* Apex.

Cytochrome enzyme   One of a series of enzymes located in the mitochondria of cells. Needed for the production of ATP during oxidative phosphorylation.

Cytochrome enzyme system   *See* Electron transport chain.

Dead space   Volume of inspired air that remains in the conducting portion of the respiratory tree (fails to reach the alveoli) and is therefore nonfunctional for gas exchange. About 150 ml.

Deoxyhemoglobin   Hemoglobin not combined with oxygen. Also called *reduced hemoglobin*.

Diaphragm   Dome-shaped sheet of skeletal muscle that separates the thoracic and abdominal cavities. The principal muscle of respiration.

Diffusion   A passive process in which there is a net movement of molecules or ions from a region of high concentration to a region of low concentration until equilibrium is reached.

Diffusion equilibrium   Equal rate of diffusion for a particular type of ion or molecule in opposite directions.

Dorsum nasi   The rounded anterior border of the nose; between the root and the apex.

Dust cell   *See* Alveolar macrophage.

Edema   An abnormal accumulation of interstitial fluid.

Electron transport chain   A chain of carrier molecules (enzymes) located on the inner membrane of a mitochondrion. As electrons are passed along the chain, energy is released for the production of ATP. Also called the *cytochrome enzyme system* and the *electron transport system*.

Electron transport system   *See* Electron transport chain.

Enzyme   A substance (usually a protein) that affects the speed of chemical changes. It does not itself undergo net change during the reaction, so it can be used many times.

Epiglottic cartilage   *See* Epiglottis.

Epiglottis   A large, leaf-shaped piece of cartilage lying on top of the larynx. Its stem portion is attached to the thyroid cartilage and its leaf portion is free to move up and down to cover the glottis (the vocal cords and the opening between them). Also called the *epiglottic cartilage*.

Erythrocyte   Red blood cell (RBC).

Erythropoiesis   The process by which erythrocytes (red blood cells) are formed.

Erythropoietin   A hormone that stimulates erythropoiesis (formation of red blood cells). It is secreted mainly by kidney cells.

Esophagus   The hollow muscular tube that connects the pharynx (throat) to the stomach.

Eupnea   Normal quiet breathing.

Exhalation   *See* Expiration.

Expiration   Breathing out. Expelling air out of the lungs into the atmosphere. Also called *exhalation*.

Expiratory area   Region of the medullary rhythmicity area that consists of expiratory neurons. They remain inactive during most normal, quiet breathing. During high levels of ventilation, impulses discharged from the expiratory area cause contraction of the internal intercostals and abdominal muscles; this leads to a decrease in the size of the thoracic cavity, and causes the forced expiration of air.

Expiratory muscles   *See* Muscles of expiration.

Expiratory neurons   Motor neurons with their cell bodies in the expiratory area of the medulla. They innervate the expiratory muscles.

Expiratory reserve volume   Volume of air in excess of the tidal volume that can be exhaled forcibly. About 1,200 ml.

External nares   Nostrils.

External respiration   The exchange of gases between the lungs and the air. Also called *pulmonary respiration*.

FAD   *See* Flavin adenine dinucleotide.

False vocal cords   *See* Ventricular folds.

Fauces   The opening from the mouth into the pharnyx.

Fissure   A groove, fold, or slit that may be normal or abnormal.

Flavin adenine dinucleotide (FAD)   A coenzyme derived from vitamin B$_2$ (riboflavin). It transfers liberated hydrogen atoms from succininc acid in the Krebs cycle to the electron transport chain. It produces one-third fewer ATPs than NAD.

Glottis   The vocal folds (true vocal cords) plus the space between them (rima glottidis).

Glucose 6-phosphate   The first intermediate metabolite in the glycolytic pathway.

Glyceraldehyde 3-phosphate   An intermediate metabolite in the glycolytic pathway. Glycerol (fat) is converted by many cells into glyceraldehyde 3-phosphate. If ATP supply is high, glyceraldehyde 3-phosphate is converted into glucose; if ATP supply is low, it is converted into pyruvic acid.

Glycogen   The major carbohydrate storage form in the body. Thousands of glucose molecules linked in a highly branched macromolecule. Most of the glycogen is stored in liver and muscle cells.

Glycolysis   Series of chemical reactions in the cytosol of a cell. In aerobic glycolysis (in the presence of oxygen), a molecule of glucose is split into two molecules of pyruvic acid; in anaerobic glycolysis (in the absence of oxygen), a molecule of glucose is split into two molecules of lactic acid.

Glycolytic pathway   The series of reactions by which one molecule of glucose is split, forming two molecules of pyruvic acid (or two molecules of lactic acid, when oxygen is not present).

Goblet cell   A specialized epithelial cell that functions as a unicellular gland; secretes mucus. Also called a *mucous cell*.

Haldane effect   In the presence of oxygen, less carbon dioxide binds to hemoglobin in the blood.

Heimlich maneuver   *See* Abdominal thrust maneuver.

Heme   Iron-containing group present in hemoglobin molecules and cytochrome enzymes.

Hemoglobin (Hb)   A molecule found in red blood cells that binds with and transports oxygen and carbon dioxide.

Hemoglobin saturation   The percent of iron atoms in a group of hemoglobin molecules that are combined with oxygen.

Henry's law   The quantity of gas that will dissolve in a liquid is directly proportional to the partial pressure of the gas and its solubility coefficient (assuming the temperature remains constant.)

Hering–Breuer reflex   *See* Inflation reflex.

Hg   The chemical symbol (abbreviation) for mercury.

Hilum   *See* Hilus.

Hilus   An area, depression, or pit where blood vessels and nerves enter and leave an organ. Also called a *hilum*.

Hypercapnia   An abnormal increase in the amount of carbon dioxide in the blood.

Hyperventilation   A rate of respiration higher than that required to maintain a normal level of plasma carbon dioxide.

Hypopharynx   *See* Laryngopharynx.

Hypoventilation   A rate of respiration lower than that required to maintain a normal level of plasma carbon dioxide.

Hypoxia   Deficiency of oxygen at the tissue level.

Inflation reflex   Reflex that prevents overinflation of the lungs. Also called *Hering–Breuer reflex*.

Inhalation   *See* Inspiration.

Inspiration   The act of drawing air from the atmosphere into the lungs. Also called *inhalation*.

Inspiratory area   Located in the medulla (brainstem). The part of the medullary rhythmicity area that determines the basic rhythm of respiration. Nerve impulses from the active inspiratory area travel to the muscles of inspiration, causing contraction; impulses last for about two seconds, then automatically stop.

Inspiratory capacity   The tidal volume plus the inspiratory reserve volume. About 3,600 ml.

Inspiratory muscles   *See* Muscles of inspiration.

Inspiratory neurons   Motor neurons with their cell bodies in the inspiratory area of the medulla (brainstem). They innervate the inspiratory muscles. Also called *medullary inspiratory neurons*.

Inspiratory reserve volume   The maximal volume of air that can be inspired over and above the resting tidal volume. About 3,100 ml.

Interalveolar septum   The wall separating adjacent alveoli. Consists of two very thin squamous epithelial cells.

Intercostal muscles   Skeletal muscles that are located between ribs (costals). Contraction of external intercostals contributes to inspiration; contraction of internal intercostals contributes to forced expiration.

Intercostal nerve   A nerve that supplies an intercostal muscle.

Intermediate metabolite   In a series of reactions (metabolic pathway), the substances (metabolites) that are not final products.

Internal nares   The two openings posterior to the nasal cavities that open into the nasopharynx. Also called the *choanae*.

Internal respiration   The exchange of respiratory gases between blood and body cells. Also called *tissue respiration*.

Intrapleural cavity   *See* Pleural cavity.

Intrapleural fluid   A film of fluid between the pleural membranes that surround the lungs. It reduces friction as the lungs expand and contract.

Intrapleural pressure   *See* Alveolar pressure.

Intrapulmonic pressure   *See* Alveolar pressure.

Krebs cycle   A series of energy-yielding chemical reactions that occur in the matrix of mitochondria. Energy is transferred to coenzymes (NAD and FAD) and carried to the electron transport chain where ATP is produced by oxidative phosphorylation. Also called the *citric acid cycle* or *tricarboxylic acid (TCA) cycle*.

Lactate   Anion (negatively charged ion) formed when lactic acid loses a hydrogen ion.

Lactic acid   A 3-carbon molecule formed by anaerobic glycolysis (in the absence of oxygen).

Laryngeal prominence   A protrusion of the anterior part of the neck caused by the thyroid cartilage.

Laryngeal sinus   The lateral expansion of the middle portion of the laryngeal cavity. Located between the vocal folds (true vocal cords) and ventricular folds (false vocal cords).

Laryngopharynx   The inferior portion of the pharynx extending downward from the level of the hyoid bone to divide posteriorly into the esophagus and anteriorly into the larynx. Also called the *hypopharynx*.

Laryngotracheal bud   In the embryo, an outgrowth of endoderm lining the digestive tract from which the respiratory system develops.

Larynx   A short passageway that connects the pharynx (throat) and the trachea. It contains the vocal cords. Also called the *voice box*.

Lingual tonsil   Aggregations of large lymphatic nodules embedded in the mucous membranes at the base of the tongue.

Lobar bronchus   *See* Secondary bronchus.

Lobe   A curved or rounded projection.

Lobule   A subdivision of a bronchopulmonary segment in the lungs. Each lobule is supplied by a branch from a terminal bronchiole.

Lower respiratory system   The larynx, trachea, bronchi, and lungs.

Lung   One of the two main organs of respiration, lying on either side of the heart in the thoracic cavity.

Lung compliance   *See* Compliance.

Meatus   A passage or opening, especially the external portion of a canal. In the nasal cavities, the meatuses are the grooves between the conchae (turbinates).

Mediastinum   A broad, median partition, actually a mass of tissue found between the pleurae of the lungs that extends from the sternum to the vertebral column.

Medulla oblongata   The most inferior part of the brain stem. Immediately superior to the spinal cord.

Medullary inspiratory neurons   *See* Inspiratory neurons.

Medullary rhythmicity area   The portion of the respiratory center in the medulla that controls the basic rhythm of respiration. Consists of two areas: (1) the inspiratory area; and (2) the expiratory area.

Metabolism   The sum of all the biochemical reactions that occur within an organism. Includes synthetic (anabolic) reactions and decomposition (catabolic) reactions.

Metabolite   Any substance produced by metabolism.

Metabolize   To change a substance by a chemical reaction in the body.

Milliliter   1/1000 of a liter. Abbreviated ml.

Minute volume of respiration (MVR)   The total volume of air taken into the lungs per minute. About 6,000 ml.

Mitochondrion   (plural: mitochondria)   A double-membraned organelle that plays a central role in the production of ATP. Known as the "powerhouse" of the cell.

Mucin   A protein found in mucus.

Mucosa   *See* Mucous membrane.

Mucous cell   *See* Goblet cell.

Mucous membrane   A membrane that lines a body cavity that opens to the exterior. Also called *mucosa*.

Mucus   The thick fluid secretion of goblet cells (mucous cells).

Muscles of expiration   Muscles involved in the forced expiration of air. Includes the internal intercostals and abdominal muscles. Also called *expiratory muscles*.

Muscles of inspiration   Muscles involved in the inspiration of air. Includes the diaphragm, external intercostals, sternocleidomastoid, scalenes, and pectoralis minor. Also called *inspiratory muscles*.

NAD   *See* Nicotinamide adenine dinucleotide.

Nares   (singular: naris)   External nares are the nostrils. Internal nares are the two openings (also called choanae) between the nasal cavities and the pharynx.

Nasal cavity   A mucous-lined cavity on either side of the nasal septum.

Nasal fossa   The portion of a nasal cavity that is anterior to the middle meatus (groove between the middle and inferior conchae).

Nasal septum   A vertical partition composed of bone (perpendicular plate of ethmoid and vomer) and cartilage that separates the nasal cavity into left and right sides.

Nasopharynx   The uppermost portion of the pharynx. Lies posterior to the nose and extends down to the soft palate.

Nicotinamide adenine dinucleotide (NAD)   A coenzyme derived from the B vitamin niacin. Used to transport hydrogen atoms from the Krebs cycle to the electron transport chain.

Nostrils   *See* Nares.

Olfactory   Pertaining to the sense of smell.

Olfactory bulb   A mass of gray matter at the termination of an olfactory nerve. Located beneath the frontal lobe of the cerebrum and above the nasal cavities.

Olfactory mucosa   The mucous membrane in the upper portion of each nasal cavity; contains receptors for the sense of smell.

Oropharynx   The middle portion of the pharynx (throat); lies posterior to the mouth and extends from the soft palate down to the hyoid bone.

Otorhinolaryngology   The branch of medicine that deals with the diagnosis and treatment of diseases of the ears, nose, and throat.

Oxaloacetic acid   A 4-carbon metabolite in the Krebs cycle. A 2-carbon acetyl group combines with oxaloacetic acid to form a 6-carbon citric acid molecule.

Oxidation   Two definitions: (1) the removal of electrons and hydrogen ions from a molecule; (2) the addition of oxygen to a molecule. Results in a decrease in the energy content of the molecule. The oxidation of glucose is called cellular respiration.

Oxidation–reduction reaction   Any reaction in which electrons are transferred from one molecule to another. The molecule that loses electrons is said to oxidized; the molecule that receives electrons is said to be reduced.

Oxidative   Using oxygen.

Oxidative phosphorylation   The addition of a phosphate group to a molecule of ADP, forming ATP. Oxygen must be present for this reaction to occur. It occurs in mitochondria in the the electron transport chain.

Oxidized   In an oxidation-reduction reaction, the molecule that loses electrons is said to be oxidized.

Oxygen debt   See Recovery oxygen consumption.

Oxygen–hemoglobin dissociation curve   A graph that shows the relationship between oxygen saturation and a variable such as temperature, pH, or plasma partial pressure.

Oxyhemoglobin   Hemoglobin combined with oxygen.

Palatine tonsils   Aggregations of large lymphatic nodules embedded in the mucous membranes lining the lateral walls of the oropharynx.

Paranasal sinus   Paired cavities lined with mucous membranes. Located in certain cranial and facial bones near the nasal cavities.

Parietal   Pertaining to the outer wall of a body cavity.

Parietal pleura   The outer layer of the serous pleural membrane that encloses and protects the lungs. The layer that is attached to the wall of the pleural cavity.

Partial pressure   The concentration of a particular gas in a mixture of gases is measured in terms of partial pressure. For example, atmospheric air has a total pressure of 760 mm Hg; air is 21% oxygen, so the partial pressure of oxygen in the air is 0.21 x 760 = 160 mm Hg.

Peripheral chemoreceptors   Receptors located in the peripheral nervous system (PNS) that are sensitive to the plasma concentrations of oxygen, carbon dioxide, and hydrogen ions. They are sensory nerve endings located in the carotid bodies and the aortic bodies.

Pharyngeal tonsil   Aggregations of large lymphatic nodules embedded in the mucous membranes of the nasopharynx. Also called the *adenoids*.

Pharynx   The throat. A tube that starts at the internal nares (choanae) and runs part way down the neck where it opens into the esophagus posteriorly and the larynx anteriorly.

Phosphorylation   The addition of a phosphate group to a chemical compound. Types of phosphorylation include: (1) substrate phosphorylation; (2) oxidative phosphorylation; and (3) photophosphorylation (in plants).

Pitch   The frequency of sound waves. The higher the frequency, the higher the pitch.

Plasma   The liquid portion of the blood.

Pleurae   See Pleural membrane.

Pleural cavity   Small potential space between the visceral and parietal pleurae. Also called the *intrapleural cavity*.

Pleural membrane   The two layers of serous membrane surrounding each lung are collectively called the pleural membrane. The outer membrane is called the parietal pleura; the inner membrane is called the visceral pleura. Also called the *pleurae*.

Pneumonia   Acute infection or inflammation of the alveoli of the lungs.

Pneumotaxic area   A group of neurons located in the upper pons. It continuously transmits inhibitory impulses to the inspiratory area (located in the medulla) that limit the duration of inspiration.

Primary bronchus   One of the two branches of the trachea. The right primary bronchus enters the right lung; the left primary bronchus enters the left lung.

Pulmonary   Pertaining to the lungs.

Pulmonary circulation   The flow of deoxygenated blood from the right ventricle of the heart to the lungs, and the return of oxygenated blood from the lungs to the left atrium.

Pulmonary edema   An abnormal accumulation of interstitial fluid in the tissue spaces and alveoli of the lungs due to increased pulmonary capillary permeability or increased pulmonary capillary pressure.

Pulmonary embolism   The presence of a blood clot or other foreign substance that obstructs the circulation of blood to lung tissue.

Pulmonary respiration   See External respiration.

Pulmonary stretch receptors   Sensory nerve endings located between the smooth muscle cells lining the airways. Unusual lung inflation stimulates these receptors, which send impulses to the medulla and inhibit the inspiratory neurons.

Pulmonary surfactant   See Surfactant.

Pulmonary trunk   The major artery that carries deoxygenated blood out of the right ventricle of the heart toward the lungs.

Pulmonary valve   One-way valve between the right ventricle of the heart and the pulmonary trunk.

Pulmonary vein   Veins that carry oxygenated blood from the lungs to the left atria of the heart.

Pulmonary ventilation   Breathing. The inflow and outflow of air between the atmosphere and the lungs. Also called *ventilation*.

Pyruvate   Anion (negatively chargen ion) formed when pyruvic acid loses a hydrogen ion.

Pyruvic acid   A 3-carbon compound that is the final product of glycolysis when oxygen is present. Pyruvic acid enters a mitochondrion and is converted into a 2-carbon acetyl group, which is carried to the Krebs cycle by coenzyme A.

Recovery oxygen consumption   The added oxygen that is taken into the body (by panting) after strenuous exercise. Previously called *oxygen debt*.

Red blood cell (RBC)   See Erythrocyte.

Reduced   In an oxidation-reduction reaction, the molecule that gains electrons is said to be reduced.

Reduced hemoglobin   See Deoxyhemoglobin.

Reduction   Two definitions: (1) the addition of electrons and hydrogen ions to a molecule; (2) the removal of oxygen from a molecule. Results in an increase in the energy content of the molecule.

Residual volume   The volume of air still contained in the lungs after a maximal expiration. About 1,200 ml.

Resistance   In lungs, the hindrance encountered by air as it moves through the respiratory passageways.

Respiration Exchange of oxygen and carbon dioxide between the atmosphere and the cells of an organism.

Respiratory acidosis Increased arterial hydrogen ion concentration due to the retention of carbon dioxide.

Respiratory alkalosis Decreased arterial hydrogen ion concentration that results when the elimination of carbon dioxide from the lungs exceeds production.

Respiratory bronchiole Branches of terminal bronchioles. Walls contain alveoli separated by cuboidal epithelial cells.

Respiratory center Neurons in the brain stem that regulate the rate of respiration. Consists of three areas: (1) the medullary rhythmicity area; (2) the pneumotaxic area; and (3) the apneustic area.

Respiratory membrane *See* Alveolar-capillary membrane.

Respiratory portion The portion of the lower respiratory tract that contains alveoli. Includes respiratory bronchioles, alveolar ducts, and alveolar sacs.

Respiratory pump The structures involved in moving air in and out of the lungs. Includes the rib cage, pleural membrane, respiratory muscles, and elastic tissues of the lungs.

Respiratory quotient (RQ) Ratio of carbon dioxide produced to oxygen consumed during metabolism.

Respiratory rate Number of breaths per minute.

Respiratory system Structures involved in gas exchange between blood and the external environment.

Rib cage *See* Thoracic cage.

Rima glottidis The opening between the vocal folds (true vocal cords).

Rima vestibuli The space between the ventricular folds (false vocal cords).

Root Of the nose: the superior attachment of the nose at the forehead between the eyes. Of the lungs: the structures entering and leaving each lung at the hilus.

Secondary bronchus A branch of a primary bronchus. The right lung has 3 secondary bronchi; the left lung has 2 secondary bronchi. Each lobe of a lung receives its own secondary (lobar) bronchus. Also called a *lobar bronchus*.

Segmental bronchus *See* Tertiary bronchus.

Septal cells *See* Type II alveolar cells.

Squamous pulmonary epithelial cells *See* Type I alveolar cells.

Stepwise A gradual progression; step by step.

Sternum A flat, elongated bone located along the midline in the anterior portion of the rib cage.

Substrate A substance that takes part in a reaction that involves enzymes.

Substrate phosphorylation A high-energy phosphate group is transferred directly from a metabolite to a molecule of ADP, forming ATP.

Succinate A 4-carbon intermediate metabolite in the Krebs cycle.

Surfactant A complex mixture of detergentlike phospholipids produced by type II alveolar cells in the lungs. It decreases the surface tension, preventing the collapse of the lungs. Also called *pulmonary surfactant*.

Terminal bronchiole Branches of bronchioles. Each lobule of a lung is supplied by one terminal bronchiole.

Tertiary bronchus A branch of a secondary bronchus. Each bronchopulmonary segment of a lung is supplied by one tertiary (segmental) bronchus. Also called a *segmental bronchus*.

Thoracic cage The skeletal portion of the chest (thorax). Also called the *rib cage*.

Thoracic cavity Superior component of the ventral body cavity. Contains two pleural cavities, the mediastinum, and the pericardial cavity.

Thoracic vertebrae The 12 vertebrae in the chest region. Each rib has a structure called a tubercle which articulates with a flat surface called a facet on a thoracic vertebra.

Thoracic wall Chest wall.

Thorax The chest.

Thyroid cartilage The largest single cartilage of the larynx (voice box). Consists of two fused plates that form the anterior wall of the larynx. Also called *Adam's apple*.

Tidal volume The volume of air breathed in and out in any one breath. About 500 ml in quiet, resting conditions.

Tissue respiration *See* Internal respiration.

Total lung capacity The sum of the tidal volume, inspiratory reserve volume, expiratory reserve volume, and the residual volume. About 6,000 ml.

Total pulmonary ventilation The total volume of air that moves in and out of the lungs in one minute. The tidal volume times the respiratory rate.

Trachea Tubular air passageway extending from the larynx to the 5th thoracic vertebra. Also called the *windpipe*.

Tricarboxylic acid cycle (TCA cycle) *See* Krebs cycle.

True vocal cords *See* Vocal folds.

Turbinate *See* Concha.

Type I alveolar cells Thin, squamous epithelial cells that line the walls of alveoli. Also called *squamous pulmonary epithelial cells*.

Type II alveolar cells Secretory cells interspersed among the type I alveolar cells that line the walls of the alveoli. They secrete surfactant, which reduces surface tension in the alveoli. Also called *septal cells*.

Upper respiratory system The nose, pharynx (throat), and associated structures.

Ventilation *See* Pulmonary ventilation.

Ventricular folds Two thick folds of mucous membrane superior to the vocal folds. Also called *false vocal cords*.

Vestibule The anterior portion of each nasal cavity just inside the nostril.

Vibrissae Hairs located in the vestibule (anterior portion) of each nostril. They remove coarse particles from incoming air.

Visceral pleura The inner layer of the serous membrane that covers each lung.

Vital capacity The sum of the tidal volume, inspiratory reserve volume, and expiratory reserve volume. About 4,800 ml.

Vocal folds A pair of mucous membrane folds below the ventricular folds (false vocal cords). Also called the *true vocal cords*.

Voice box *See* Larynx.

Windpipe *See* Trachea.

Bibliography

Curtis, Helena.   *Biology,* 3rd ed.
New York : Worth, 1979.

Dorland, William Alexander.   *Dorland's Illustrated Medical Dictionary,* 27th ed.
Philadelphia : W. B. Saunders, 1988.

Ganong, William F.   *Review of Medical Physiology,* 15th ed.
Norwalk, Connecticut : Appleton & Lange, 1991.

Goldberg, Stephen.   *Clinical Anatomy Made Ridiculously Simple.*
Miami, Florida : MedMaster, 1984.

Junqueira, L. Carlos, Jose Carneiro, and Robert O. Kelley.   *Basic Histology,* 6th ed.
Norwalk, Connecticut : Appleton & Lange, 1989.

Kimball, John W.   *Biology,* 4th ed.
Reading, Massachusetts : Addison-Wesley, 1978.

Melloni, B.J., Ida Dox, and Gilbert Eisner.   *Melloni's Illustrated Medical Dictionary,* 2nd ed.
Baltimore : Williams & Wilkins, 1992.

Moore, Keith L.   *Clinically Oriented Anatomy,* 3rd ed.
Baltimore : Williams & Wilkins, 1992.

Netter, Frank H.   *Atlas of Human Anatomy.*
Summit, N.J. : Ciba - Geigy, 1989.

Tortora, Gerard J. and Sandra Reynolds Grabowski.   *Principles of Anatomy and Physiology,* 7th ed.
New York : HarperCollins, 1993.

Vander, Arthur J., James H. Sherman, and Dorothy S. Luciano.   *Human Physiology,* 5th ed.
New York : McGraw-Hill, 1990.